GREEN ENERGY

GREEN ENERGY

A non-nuclear response to the
greenhouse effect

DAVE TOKE

First published in 1990 by
Green Print
an imprint of The Merlin Press
10 Malden Road, London NW5 3HR

ISBN 185425 035 3

1 2 3 4 5 6 7 8 9 10 :: 99 98 97 96 95 94 93 92 91 90

Phototypeset by Input Typesetting, London

Printed and bound in England by Biddles Ltd., Guildford and King's
Lynn on recycled paper

Contents

NOTES TO READERS

This book is published by Green Print in co-operation with the Socialist Environment and Resources Association, 11 Goodwin Street, London N4 3HQ.

The views expressed are solely those of the author, and do not necessarily represent the views of SERA or of individual SERA members.

All energy statistics given in this book are based on data from *The BP Statistical Review of World Energy*, except where otherwise stated.

Please refer to the Glossary at the end of the book for an explanation of some of the abbreviations and terms used in the text.

Introduction

In recent times 'saving the planet' has become central to a new political consciousness in Britain. Yet while there may be a common acceptance of underlying causes of incipient catastrophe there is, predictably, no consensus regarding solutions.

Many people have become committed to making their own individual contributions, particularly in the area of product choice – from washing up liquid to unleaded petrol. Other people are convinced that only a no growth strategy and a return to simple lifestyles can sufficiently reverse the polluting path of industrialised society. Most people, however, hope that it will be possible to improve lifestyles, while limiting pollution. They look to governments to find the way forward.

The challenge lies in how to restructure industry and lifestyles, without impoverishment, so that they become sustainable in ecological terms. The issue of energy policy is central to the debate about sustainability. Without energy nothing moves, yet quite clearly we are already using far too much. If we in the developed world do not drastically reduce the amount of pollution we are creating we cannot expect the developing world to hold back and not exacerbate global warming caused, amongst other things, by fossil fuel emissions.

It should be obvious to everyone by now that our first priority must be energy conservation. We live in a society conspicuous for its waste, and the wastage of energy is simply appalling. So much can be achieved already. Much more could be achieved if science and industry were prodded into making energy efficiency much more of a priority than it is now. To many people the notion of 'green nuclear power' is laughably bizarre. Indeed it is, but we do need to derive non-fossil sources of energy from somewhere. We must argue that this energy should come from natural, not nuclear sources. There are boundless opportunities for this and we should eagerly seize the opportunities that are already at hand as well as spending a lot more money on research and development.

All this needs intervention and planning, albeit on a decentralised rather than a 'big brother' basis. Traditional socialism has been about caring for other people and organising society in such a way as to achieve this. It is no surprise that the idealism of green politics, which is about caring for the planet, coexists much more easily with socialist ideas rather than the hedonistic materialism of the Thatcherite philosophy.

This book is a vital practical contribution to the debate about what action is required to save the planet. Many of the proposals made in the text that follows are controversial for all parties. Only time and further discussion will tell whether they have validity, but I am certain that discussion of the ideas raised by this book cannot and must not be avoided.

Joan Ruddock

(Joan Ruddock MP is a vice-president of the Socialist Environment and Resources Association.)

1 Energy and Sustainability

The world is facing a growing ecological crisis caused by the effects of gaseous emissions from the activities of Homo sapiens. The biggest single source of these gaseous emissions is the fossil fuel we burn to provide us with energy.

It is looking more and more probable that the various gases produced, acting like glass in a greenhouse, are heating up the world's atmosphere. This global warming is likely to produce rising sea levels and shifting rainfall patterns. This will have disastrous social and political consequences.

The lives and livelihoods of large sections of the world's population will be threatened as flooding, extreme climatic fluctuations and changes in agricultural patterns disrupt societies across the planet.

This book looks at ways in which we can, through changes in this country's use and production of energy, contribute to the task of slowing down the greenhouse effect.[1] We are not going to stop global warming entirely, but we can minimise its effects and slow down its impact to allow time for human, plant and animal life to adjust to greenhouse induced changes in the ecosphere.

Many other environmental problems including acid rain, water pollution, soil erosion and deforestation are consequences of the same practices and policies that are heating up the planet. If we gear our policies to tackling global warming, we shall also ameliorate many of these other environmental problems. Energy practices, and for that matter other practices, which fail to tackle the greenhouse effect are unsustainable.

SUSTAINABILITY

A sustainable energy strategy is one that can be continued into the indefinite future. A sustainable energy policy must have an anti-greenhouse strategy at its heart.

Given the finite nature of fossil fuel resources and the likelihood that global disaster through greenhouse induced warming will drastically disrupt human society before such resources are exhausted, present and conventionally projected future patterns of fossil fuel consumption are unsustainable. I would also argue that the use of nuclear power as even only a partial response to global warming is unsustainable.

Reliance on nuclear energy means reliance not only on an energy source, uranium, that is itself finite, but also on an energy source that brings with it the insoluble problem of nuclear waste, the risks of horrific accidents and the political dangers of nuclear proliferation and nuclear terrorism. When even only a few of the more quantifiable environmental problems of nuclear power are incorporated into the cost structure of the nuclear industry the whole process looks hopelessly uneconomic. For example, the revelations about the true cost of nuclear waste disposal and decommissioning of nuclear power stations seems, at the time of writing, to have sounded the death-knell for the British nuclear power industry. Even the more esoteric and underdeveloped renewable technologies begin to look attractive by comparison.

I reject the notion that there is no alternative to a nuclear strategy outside of a drastic curtailment of living standards. There is a sustainable energy path that relies, in the long term, on renewable energy (natural sources of energy which do not run out), and allows rising living standards.

I argue in this book that we must start a transition to this future now. This involves reducing the use of fossil fuels in the context of a non-nuclear energy strategy that prioritises energy efficiency and the deployment of renewable energy sources.

This is a path that involves radical choices for us all, including those on the left whose traditional attachment to coal must not blind them to the need to reduce the burning of coal as well as oil and gas. It is a path that forces us to reduce pollution from motor vehicles. Present, never mind projected future levels of motor car pollution and motor car use are unsustainable.

What is clear to greens, and increasingly clear to others in the political mainstream, is that sustainability has not been the overriding criterion of energy policy in the past. Moreover, it has hardly been accorded any sort of priority at all.

Sustainability cannot be the only criterion of energy policy, but it must be the overriding criterion, to which all other criteria must be subsumed. There is also a need to devise a transitional strategy to take us from the unsustainable practices of the present to the sustainability of the future.

Most greens, of whatever hue, whether 'light' or 'dark', to use Jonathon Porritt's typology,[2] believe that people should enjoy basic necessities including warmth, light and energy for cooking, although interpretations of what this means and entails will vary.

Socialists will stress the need for the community to guarantee the provision of basic energy needs, and that whilst energy conservation is an overriding priority, it should not be pursued at the expense of the poor.

What is more at issue is whether the criterion of sustainability allows for continued growth in the production of goods and services in the already industrialised nations of the world, including the UK.

I believe that it is possible to achieve at least modest growth in the context of the type of sustainable development described by the UN-sponsored Brundtland Report. We must fight the poverty that is present in both the industrialised world and the developing world. As Brundtland commented:

> A world in which poverty is endemic will always be prone to ecological and other catastrophes.[3]

It is misleading to see the pursuit of sustainable policies in terms of seeking the 'purest' green solution. There are real left or right wing choices that still have to be made. Is conservation to be achieved at the expense of the poor? Should environmental protection programmes be paid for through extra taxation or through cutbacks in existing social spending? Green politics undoubtedly adds a new dimension to politics, but it is one which supplements rather than displaces the existing left-right axis.

Socialists will choose the options that produce egalitarian results. Green socialists will argue that sustainability is best achieved in the context of democratic control of the economy, although the appalling environmental record of the Soviet bloc suggests that we should opt for decentralised, democratic socialism rather than centralised Marxist-Leninism.

However, whatever political vehicles we choose, all greens will be at one in accepting the pressing need to fundamentally change the nature of industrial society to make our activities many times more energy and resource efficient and much less polluting.

I shall move on to outline the objectives and some of the practicalities of a sustainable energy policy for the UK, but before doing even this it is relevant to take a brief look at the main factors which have influenced the energy industry in the UK since the end of World War Two.

PAST INFLUENCES ON THE ENERGY INDUSTRY

This country has had little that has resembled a coherent set of objectives that one would call an energy policy, although the stated policy of the Attlee government, which nationalised the main energy industries, was to arrive at an integrated energy policy.

The practice then and thereafter has had little to do with the pursuit of a rational set of objectives and much more with a competition for advantage between the different sectors of the energy industry and the interest groups involved in them.

Governments have pursued a vague objective of securing the cheapest cost of energy supply and of trying to make the nationalised industries break even, although the interpretation of these objectives has varied considerably. The Thatcher government says it wants the market to decide priorities. It has privatised gas and electricity, with coal clearly in its sights if it wins the next general election.

Tony Benn, Energy Secretary from 1975–79, has been the only recent Energy Minister to have talked about having a full blown energy policy, although he did not achieve his target. On the other hand Nigel Lawson, during his brief spell as Energy Minister, seemed to deny that the government even wanted to have an energy policy.[4] The present government has advocated leaving things to the market, a policy which conflicted with support for nuclear power. In fact no totally privately financed nuclear power station has been ordered, and completed, since 1974 throughout the whole of the world. The government could not sell nuclear power to the city as part of the electricity privatisation package. This failure has brought the already stumbling British nuclear programme to its knees.

The government continues to support nuclear power by requiring the electricity industry to use a non-fossil fuel quota, the extra costs being paid for through the non-fossil fuel levy. Without this protection, market forces would ensure a rapid phase-out of nuclear power.

The contradictions of proposing privatisation and attempting to support nuclear power at the same time have become abundantly clear. Many accused Friends of the Earth of being machiavellian when they decided, in early 1988, to back electricity privatisation because it would scupper nuclear power. We may disagree with the idea of privatisation, but we cannot fault the percipient nature of Friends of the Earth's reasoning!

The government are not at all clear as to how a free market in energy, even if such a thing is achievable, can guarantee the attainment of environmental objectives. The government does not have the unanimous support of even the Conservative Party for its attempts to minimise state intervention in the energy market. The Select Committee on Energy, with its Conservative majority, has issued calls for intervention to promote energy conservation.[5]

Although we cannot speak of this country having an energy policy in the sense of a clear set of objectives, various influences on the energy industry can be observed. The way I order them does not indicate their relative importance.

First is the idea of political security. Following the first oil crisis of 1973 this country sought to reduce its reliance on foreign oil, although the prospect of North Sea oil and the existence of around 300 years of coal reserves made the UK position less critical than that of many others. However, the need to rely more on coal than on oil for electricity production increased the attractiveness of the nuclear power option for Conservatives who wished to spike the guns of the miners, their most fearsome political adversaries.

In October 1979 the Conservative cabinet agreed to a programme of building ten big PWR nuclear reactors, one a year from 1982. According to a leaked cabinet minute:

> . . . a nuclear programme would have the advantage of removing a substantial portion of electricity production from the dangers of disruption by industrial action by coal miners or transport workers.[6]

Second are the resources of the country. It is no wonder that the UK is more dependent on coal than other European countries considering its large coal reserves. Since the 1960s natural gas has increased its penetration of the energy market with the exploitation of North Sea resources. Yet this country has among the world's largest wind, wave and tidal resources, and they remain untouched.

Third are the various pressures from interest groups. These have included the nationalised industries, but also the oil companies whose influence on the UK government has been regarded as considerable by other European nations. The nuclear energy lobby has had a pervasive influence on the UK's electricity supply industry.

Fourth has been the convenience of the energy supplies themselves. Electricity's use has been favoured by this factor, and so has oil whose use in transportation is essential for most purposes.

Fifth has been the economics of the energy industry. Crucially, this concerns the cost of supply, although this involves a range of factors including investment decisions, pricing structure, tax policies and marketing strategy. Investment decisions have advantaged nuclear power, but disadvantaged renewables.

The fact that oil undermined coal as the principal world energy source in the 1950s and 1960s is at least partly attributable to the practice of oil companies selling off the heavier fuel oils cheaply to industry after the lighter oils had been taken to meet the ever-growing demand for petrol.

Environmental considerations have rarely, at least in this country, featured as important influences on the energy supply industries, except perhaps as a means of helping oil companies brush up their image in advertisements. But now everyone seems to be falling over themselves to justify their own interests in environmental terms.

We are moving towards seeing sustainability as the key, overriding objective, although we are as yet a long way from turning the generalised rhetoric of politicians into real action. In making this transition we need to find yardsticks to measure our progress towards sustainability. The yardsticks provided by the need to combat the greenhouse effect are crucially important in any discussion of a sustainable energy strategy. Others which should be added include the combatting of acid rain, the avoidance of the dangers of radiation and the avoidance of pollution from new energy sources.

In order to devise policies capable of reducing greenhouse emissions, we have to identify the sources of the problem.

GREENHOUSE GASES

Different gases will have different warming effects, but in terms of their contribution to new warming the proportions in the 1980s were roughly as shown in Table 1.1.

Table 1.1: Relative contributions of trace gases to new global warming	
Carbon dioxide	50%
Methane	18%
Nitrous Oxide	6%
Chlorofluorocarbons (CFCs)	14%
Surface ozone etc.	12%
Total	100%

Source: Stewart Boyle and John Ardill, The Greenhouse Effect, *London, New English Library, 1989.*

The atmospheric concentration of carbon dioxide, which is the single biggest contributor to global warming, has increased from about 270 parts per million before the industrial revolution to about 350 parts per million now. The concentration is increasing by about 1½ parts per million per year.

The sizes of the relative contributions to new global warming are changing, but even if current efforts to eliminate ozone-eating CFCs are successful, recent rates of growth in world energy consumption (about 2 per cent per year) will produce a global warming of between 1.5 and 4.5 degrees Celsius by about 2040.[7]

There is a degree of uncertainty in such calculations, but a 3° rise in global temperature, greater at the poles and less at the equator, is a rough mean of the various estimates.

Given that there is a time-lag in the operation of the greenhouse effect because of the time it takes for the oceans to warm, a decision to wait until the message of global warming is abundantly clear would be quite literally too late. In fact the world has warmed by at least half a degree over the past century. The warming trend could be caused by factors other than an increase in the greenhouse effect, but it can definitely be said that global warming over the last hundred years is consistent with the greenhouse effect hypothesis.

Recently analysed geological evidence also supports the now well developed theory of global warming. Over the past several hundred thousand years it seems that rises in atmospheric carbon dioxide levels have preceded temperature rises.[8]

Another relatively recent advance has been in 'chaos' theory. This suggests that changes in global temperature could have very large impacts on climatic patterns as weather patterns may 'flip' from one stable state to another. Ice ages seem to have been triggered by relatively small initial falls in temperature. The likely rate of current global warming is far more rapid than the cooling which triggered the ice ages.

At the depths of the last ice age, the world was only 4°C cooler than it is today.

Even if the rate of warming is only towards the lower end of the estimates of global warming, the effects on sea levels and climates will be very great indeed. The UK will suffer from coastal flooding and inundation of low-lying areas and it will suffer indirectly from social destabilisation in other parts of the world.

Rainfall patterns are very responsive to small changes in temperature. Half the world's population is dependent on current rainfall patterns. If these change suddenly, massive migrations will result with incalculable social, economic and political consequences.

The effect of rapid change on many types of plant and animal life will be deadly since for many species the rate of change will be much faster than their ability to adapt to new circumstances.

In the 1970s the developing ecology movement justified the need for energy conservation and the development of alternative energy sources on the grounds that energy resources were being rapidly depleted. But the threat from greenhouse warming has made these concerns seem minor by comparison. What is perhaps not yet fully understood is that we simply cannot afford to even come close to exhausting world fossil fuel resources.

Even if we only used up *half* the world's coal resources, so much carbon dioxide would be emitted that the planet would probably be warmed by around six degrees, *not counting* the warming effect of other greenhouse gases (see Table 1.1). The resultant warming effects would blow the fuses of most of the computerised models of the world climate system used to make predictions about the climatic consequences of global warming.

What is clear is that the world's ecosphere would, by today's standards, become completely unrecognisable.

SOURCES OF GASES

Carbon dioxide comes mainly from burning fossil fuels (coal, oil, gas), but around a quarter of it comes from the burning of the tropical rainforests.

Methane comes mainly from rotting rice paddies and ruminating cows; food production to feed the world's fast expanding population. A rather smaller amount is emitted as a result of extraction and transport of natural gas and coal. Significant amounts of methane are released from rubbish tips.

Nitrous oxide comes partly from fossil fuel burning and partly from artificial fertilisers.

CFCs come from aerosol cans, which are being rapidly phased out, foamed plastics, refrigerators and industrial cleaning.

Ozone in the lower atmosphere is produced mainly by sunlight reacting with various emissions from motor vehicles.

Over half of global warming results from fossil fuels and is caused by a combination of carbon dioxide, ozone, nitrous oxide and methane produced by fossil fuel burning and, to a small extent, its extraction.

Because the biggest contributor to global warming is fossil fuel emission, an anti-greenhouse strategy must be one which reduces carbon dioxide and nitrous oxide emissions and cuts down on other fossil fuel derived pollutants that promote ozone formation.

However the industrialised quarter of the world must also be aware of the need to avoid food, trade, aid and money-lending policies which encourage developing countries to destroy trees and create deserts.

INTERNATIONAL CO-OPERATION

International negotiations about saving the ozone layer from attack by rising levels of CFCs have demonstrated the need for global co-operation so that developing countries can achieve higher living standards without disrupting the ecosphere.

Yet, at least at the time of writing, both the UK government and the European Community have so far refused to support the setting up of an international climate protection fund to help the Chinese and others use substitutes for CFCs in their fridges. Such a fund is essential if we are to tackle global climatic problems and, for example, offer assistance to developing nations to invest in energy efficiency and renewable energy technologies.

It has been suggested that such a fund could be created by establishing an international fossil fuel tax. Apart from the lack of a global administrative structure, such a scheme could create serious shortages and exacerbate ecological destruction in poor developing nations who may be already destroying their environmental resources to obtain the foreign exchange to pay for oil and other raw materials.

It would be rather more practical for nations to contribute to the fund in proportion to their own energy consumption, or in proportion to their own gross domestic products. The different countries could raise this money by means of their own choosing, although doing it by energy taxation would seem to be the most obvious course. Higher levels of energy taxation including 'carbon taxes' could encourage fuel switching and help reduce energy consumption in the industrialised world.

The green movement must press governments to negotiate a protocol setting global and, perhaps more importantly, national targets for reductions in fossil fuel emissions. Such negotiations will be difficult and complex and agreement will be harder to reach on this issue than was the case even with the very partial agreements reached so far on CFCs.

However, it has to be done and the sooner we start the sooner a really concentrated effort can be made to tackle the problem. The United Nations Environment Programme hopes that some sort of concordat can be formulated by 1992. Then again, an effective response to global warming requires much more than even emission reduction targets. The approach must be one that simultaneously attacks the interlocking crises that are producing accelerating ecological destruction.

In 1980 the Brandt Report advocated that the industrialised nations give aid to the South, saying that the northern hemisphere would also benefit because of the increased trade that would result. However, despite the Report's critical acclaim it was not implemented, partly because of the devastating second oil crisis, partly because of a new round of cold war confrontation, but also because the South simply had no leverage on the North to force it to come to terms.

The greenhouse effect adds a new dimension to the situation. The developing and industrialised world must come to a deal that will safeguard the planet's future. There is no alternative for anyone.

The outlines of a possible North/South deal are becoming increasingly clear. The developing nations should take urgent action to stop the destruction of the rainforests and should seek to achieve sustainable development in the context of energy conservation and the deployment of renewable energy sources. The industrialised world should cancel debts of developing nations, reform and expand international aid, end their protectionist food policies, seek to alter the trade system more in favour of poorer nations, and themselves adopt sustainable energy and industrial strategies.

Of course such an approach should not exclude unilateral action. Debt cancellation, for example, is urgently required to stop the madcap outflow of money from poor to rich countries, an outflow largely based on accelerating ecological destruction. Yet the 1989 Paris Economic Summit, billed as the 'green summit', ignored the realities of the global crisis, shunned any notion of large-scale debt cancellations and concentrated on how to increase the largesse already at the disposal of the richest nations.

The UK's record on aid is particularly poor. In 1987 we gave only 0.28 per cent of our gross domestic product in foreign aid, well short of the UN target of 0.7 per cent. Most of this aid is tied up in deals that seem to benefit this country's trading and economy rather than that of the recipient country. Many of the development projects supported by the UK, the International Monetary Fund and the World Bank involve various types of environmental destruction, including deforestation.

Current aid levels are extremely puny compared to the levels of Marshall Aid given to Europe soon after World War Two. Such aid was largely unspecific, giving the European nations foreign exchange to pay for raw materials in an effort to stave off national bankruptcies. Yet the growing global ecological crisis threatens to bankrupt the entire world in physical terms, which will in itself trigger off economic, political and social crises in both developed and developing nations.

If we do not give developing countries sufficient help then rises in sea levels will occur faster than our ability to adapt to them. Large tracts of East Anglia and other places will be lost and the more established agricultural and social patterns will be disrupted.

The social and political chaos that will surely result from large scale population migrations in the developing world brought on by shifting rainfall patterns will destabilise the world's political economy affecting the stability even of richer nations.

Massive increases in unspecific aid are what developing countries need, as well as help from funds, such as a climate protection fund, which would be set up to give aid for specific projects that encourage sustainable development.

Such actions would increase the ability of the developing nations to resist the deadly embrace of multinational corporations who so often offer development at the cost of ecological devastation. The European Community has a potentially crucial role to play if it can control or at least regulate multinationals who wish to take advantage of European markets or capital.

The thawing of the cold war creates a good atmosphere of global accord. Green pressure for action is growing in most nations. Climate protection will cost the industrialised world a lot of money, but such expenditure is a small price to pay to stave off the consequences of inaction. If the North does not accede to the call to help, then the planet will be in grave peril, for the developing world does not, on its own, have the money to foot the bill to save it.

The industrialised world must help the developing world improve its living standards as part of a strategy to reduce population pressures. We must also shift to organic farming methods and of course eliminate CFC production as rapidly as possible.

Yet whatever changes in the world trading and monetary systems are wrought and whatever levels of international aid for sustainable development may be attained, the fight will be lost unless the industrialised nations themselves re-order their own economies and lifestyle patterns, and in particular adopt sustainable energy policies.

Unless the first and second worlds can do this, and in the process achieve very high levels of energy efficiency and reliance on renewable energy sources, then the third world will have no alternative but to industrialise along the same pollution-strewn path already beaten flat by the developed world.

I shall now turn to the specific details of adopting a sustainable energy strategy in the UK and begin by looking at the nature of the problem in terms of carbon dioxide pollution levels.

ENERGY CONSUMPTION AND CARBON PRODUCTION

Three-quarters of the world's energy-related carbon dioxide emissions come from the industrialised peoples who make up one quarter of the world. Around 27 per cent of the carbon dioxide comes from North America, 25 per cent from Eastern Europe and 15 per cent from Western Europe. China with a quarter of the world's population produces about 9 per cent of global carbon dioxide emissions, while the United Kingdom with 1 per cent of the world's people produces about 3 per cent of the carbon dioxide.

The breakdown of 1987 primary energy consumption on a fuel by fuel basis in Western Europe and the UK is as follows.

Table 1.2: Fuel by fuel breakdown of UK and European energy consumption

	W. Europe	UK
oil	45%	36%
natural gas	16%	24%
coal	20%	33%
hydroelectricity	8%	1%
nuclear electricity	11%	6%
Total	100%	100%

Source: B.P. Statistical Review of World Energy, 1988.

While 35 per cent of UK primary energy goes into making electricity, under 40 per cent of this is actually turned into electrical energy.

About three-quarters of UK electricity comes from coal fired power stations, with nuclear providing the bulk of the rest alongside some from oil and hydropower sources. Recently the CEGB has been showing greater interest in gas turbines and to a lesser extent in wind power.

In 1987 electricity production accounted for 39 per cent of the UK's output of carbon dioxide.

As can be seen from Figure 1.1, by far the largest single source of carbon dioxide emissions in the UK, in terms of fuel, is coal, with coal for electricity making up the bulk of this. Coal's proportional contribution to carbon dioxide emissions is larger than its actual proportion of total primary energy consumption because burning coal emits larger quantities of carbon dioxide than burning oil and natural gas.

As an approximate guide, for a given amount of energy output, coal will produce 100 units of carbon dioxide compared to 80 units from oil and 60 units from gas (see Figure 1.2). The differing efficiencies of different types of power stations alter these figures, generally to the benefit of natural gas.

We can see from Figure 1.1, that the electricity production sector is the biggest emitter of carbon dioxide followed by industry, then transport and then the domestic and commercial/public sectors.

These sectoral contributions to total carbon dioxide need to be put into perspective by looking at the rates of change in the various sectors over recent years. We can do this by looking at Table 1.3.

Many sectoral contributions to carbon dioxide production have remained fairly constant; the exceptions are industry, which declined dramatically because of the recession and the loss of many of the UK's energy intensive heavy industries, and road transport, which is increasing at a very dramatic and indeed alarming rate.

REDUCING CARBON DIOXIDE EMISSIONS

In June 1988 the Toronto Conference on the Changing Atmosphere called for a 20 per cent reduction in world carbon dioxide emissions by 2005. It also called for a cut of 50 per cent in carbon dioxide emissions in the longer term.

Emissions by Fuel Type

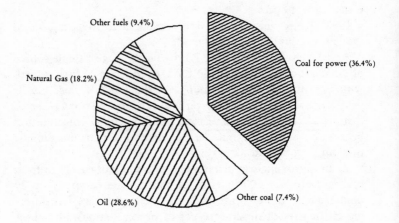

Other fuels (9.4%)

Coal for power (36.4%)

Natural Gas (18.2%)

Oil (28.6%)

Other coal (7.4%)

Emissions by Sector

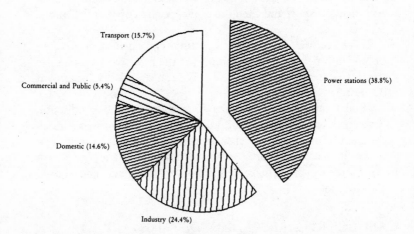

Transport (15.7%)

Power stations (38.8%)

Commercial and Public (5.4%)

Domestic (14.6%)

Industry (24.4%)

Figure 1.1: Estimated breakdown of CO_2 emissions in the UK (1987). [Source: Memorandum from Friends of the Earth to the Commons Select Committee on Energy on Implications of the Greenhouse Effect for UK Energy Policy, London, Friends of the Earth, 1989, page 6.]

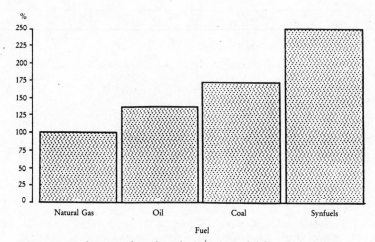

Figure 1.2: Relative carbon dioxide emissions of different fuels. [Source: Association for the Conservation of Energy; Evidence to the House of Commons Select Committee on Energy's Enquiry into the Energy Policy Implications of the Greenhouse Effect, memoranda page 4, London, HMSO, 1989.]

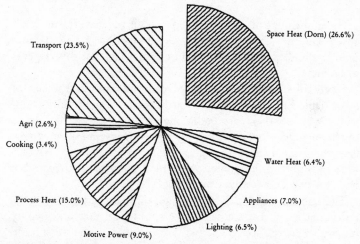

Figure 1.3: Estimated CO_2 emissions by end-use (1987). [Source: T. Jackson, The role of nuclear power in global warming abatement strategies, proof of evidence to Hinkley 'C' nuclear power station enquiry, London, Friends of the Earth, 1989, p. 21.]

TABLE 1.3: UK CO$_2$ emissions by weight
million tonnes (1977, 1983 and 1987).

Sector	1977	1983	1987	Per cent change from 1977 to 1987
Power stations	238	221	233	−2
Industry[1]	170	123	125	−26
Road transport	73	82	98	+34
Domestic	85	81	87	+2
Commercial/public	34	33	32	−6
Refineries	25	21	21	−1
Others[2]	28	30	31	+10

[1] Excludes cement and energy industries.
[2] Includes cement, gas production and flaring.

Source: adapted from House of Commons Select Committee on Energy, Energy Policy Implications of the Greenhouse Effect, London, HMSO, 1989, p. 18.

Given the huge disparity in energy usage between the industrialised and developing nations, the reduction required from industrialised nations is likely to be rather larger if this target is to be met.

Florentin Krause and others of the International Project for Sustainable Energy Paths[9] say that European Community countries can reduce their carbon dioxide production from fossil fuels by 80 per cent over fifty years while maintaining economic growth. They believe that this would contribute to a world strategy limiting the global warming commitment to between one and two degrees by around 2050.

They recommend that the biggest priority should be more efficient energy use. Secondly we should develop and deploy renewable energy sources. Thirdly we should, in the short term, switch from coal and oil to gas since gas produces much less carbon dioxide than oil and coal.

In fact this strategy would demand a highly dramatic alteration in patterns of energy use. However, it would not necessarily require abandoning the high standards of living to which at least some of us in the West are accustomed.

Contrary to popular belief, rising living standards do not automatically mean higher energy usage. Since the oil price rises of the 1970s, energy growth in the member states of the Organisation for Economic Co-operation and Development has slowed considerably. In 1987 the UK actually consumed 8 per cent *less* primary energy than it did in 1973, despite economic growth of 25 per cent in real terms since 1973.

Although the oil price rises did encourage major gains in energy efficiency, the slowdown in energy growth in the West is also attributable to the recessions which were triggered by the oil crises. In addition to this, in the UK as in many other advanced industrial nations there has been a shift away from energy-intensive heavy industries like steelmaking towards lighter industries like electronics and towards service industries.

In the most recent period western energy consumption has once more started to rise. In fact in 1988 world energy consumption rose by nearly 4 per cent compared to 1987. This is approaching the rates reached before the first oil crisis in 1973. If such a level of increase continued it would accelerate greenhouse warming at a calamitous speed. In reality such a rate of energy growth would almost certainly be cut short sooner or later by a fresh oil crisis.

There are very big potentials for cutting out the tremendous energy wastage that occurs in the industrialised economies. A big problem facing any negotiations on a global level to cut carbon dioxide emissions is that energy growth is rising fastest in the developing nations. Given that they are way behind the developed countries in terms of living standards it will be virtually impossible to ask them not to increase their carbon dioxide emissions without massive assistance from the developed world.

The industrialised nations must radically reduce their fossil fuel emissions and help developing nations use energy efficiently as well as assisting their deployment of renewable energy sources.

Energy conservation and deployment of renewable energy sources will be the main planks of sustainable energy strategy throughout the world. Beyond this, varying social conditions and energy resources mean that there is no all-encompassing blueprint. It is, if I can be excused for using what has now become a cliché, a case of 'thinking globally and acting locally'. The UK should look towards implementing the sort of approach described by Florentin Krause.

The achievement of such a strategy would require some very fundamental changes in policies and attitudes, and some painful political reappraisals on the left as well as the right of the political spectrum.

Although coal will remain a major contributor to primary energy consumption for a long time to come, it must be steadily displaced by a combination of the three strategies mentioned above, especially in the case of the UK which, as Table 1.2 shows, consumes coal at well above the average rate for European countries.

Oil consumption must also be reduced until we reach a situation where it is conserved for use in transportation and as an industrial feedstock. In the farther-flung future it should be possible to reduce oil in transport with power from renewable resources and oil based plastics with biodegradable products made from plants.

If we are to meet the carbon dioxide emission reduction targets advocated by the Toronto Conference, and do so as well as phasing out nuclear power, we need as much energy conservation and renewable energy as we can muster.

Can an anti-greenhouse strategy afford to be non-nuclear?

2   Nuclear Power is no Answer

The withdrawal of nuclear power from the sell-off of the electricity supply industry and the cancellation of at least three of the proposed pressurised water reactors has dealt a severe blow to the prospects of the British nuclear power industry. Without the new reactors, the proportion of electricity coming from nuclear power will decline.

Nevertheless, despite its low morale, the nuclear industry still hopes to stage a comeback. The UK's electricity industry is dominated by a pro-nuclear establishment which is still urging investment in nuclear power as a means of combatting the greenhouse effect. However, many dispute the claim that building more nuclear power stations is an acceptable way to combat global warming.

Krause and his colleagues, along with others such as Keepin and Kats[1] argue that nuclear power is not a feasible option for reducing carbon dioxide emissions because of its extremely high costs compared to other strategies, and because of its disadvantageous environmental impacts.

Keepin and Kats say that with current energy growth rates continuing into the future the world would need to build about 5000 nuclear power stations, one every two and a half days, by 2025 to replace energy supply that would otherwise come from coal. Even then carbon dioxide emissions would be slightly more than at present.

Investment in the most energy efficient lighting systems, water heaters, refrigerators, heat pumps and other equipment will reduce emissions nearly seven times more effectively than investment in nuclear power stations.

Of course this argument does not remove the need for some

new non-fossil generating capacity to take the place of some of the retiring fossil fuel power stations that are becoming too expensive to run. But this does not mean that nuclear power is essential or necessary, since we can develop non-greenhouse inducing renewable energy sources instead. It does mean that we must not only pursue a conservationist strategy, but we must also vigorously encourage the development and deployment of renewable energy sources.

In environmental and political terms nuclear power compares highly unfavourably with the renewable developments suggested in this book. Nuclear power is beset by problems involving nuclear safety, nuclear waste disposal, the decommissioning of nuclear power stations, nuclear weapons proliferation and the security of fissile materials.

There were two partial core meltdowns in nuclear reactors in the first four thousand reactor years of world nuclear power. Three Mile Island in the USA in 1979 and Chernobyl in 1986. This excludes the 1957 Windscale fire which occurred at a military reactor. Five thousand nuclear reactors would, on this basis, produce two or three meltdowns a year.

In 1986 the CEGB estimated that between 10,000 and 36,000 people in Russia and Europe would die from cancers brought on by radiation from the Chernobyl accident.[2] Since then the estimates of cancer deaths brought on by a given amount of radiation have been revised upwards meaning that even the figure of 36,000 cancer deaths may be an underestimate.

Some environmentalists have urged a rethink of nuclear power in the light of the greenhouse effect. Researchers like David Cope suggest that we should develop safer forms of nuclear power.[3]

Even if we do have 'safe' reactors (and if reactors can be immunised against the consequences of human error), there are still many problems with the industry, not the least the sheer financial cost of making them environmentally acceptable. Phasing out nuclear power now prevents us from being locked into a strategy that will see these problems grow.

At a time when people around the world are making more strident demands on industry to alter their methods to reduce the production of toxic wastes, the nuclear industry can do nothing to stop such production. In fact reprocessing and the development of fast breeder reactors will serve to dramatically increase the production of nuclear waste material.

Nuclear power is limited by the fact that it can only produce electric energy, which even in this country only accounts for about 15 per cent of the energy actually supplied to consumers (delivered energy). In no way could it ever be an 'answer' to the greenhouse effect.

In theory we could have an 'all electric', nuclear powered economy, but, as I argue later, the world will experience serious uranium depletion problems at levels of uranium consumption of only a fraction of what would be required to run a mainly nuclear electric world energy economy.

Furthermore, developing countries find it difficult to afford the cost of nuclear power as it is very capital-intensive. Thus nuclear technology would largely have to be deployed by the industrialised nations who should really be leading the way in using conservation and renewable technologies like solar power, techniques that will be rather more useful to the developing world than nuclear power.

Dr Nigel Mortimer, in a paper for Friends of the Earth,[4] suggested that nuclear power is not quite as carbon-free as it appears. This is because large amounts of energy are expended in mining and processing uranium ore.

With high grade ore this means that a 1000MW nuclear power station will generate only about 4 per cent of the carbon dioxide generated by an equivalently rated conventional coal station. But a wind power or tidal power scheme would generate about 1 per cent, and investment in insulation less than 0.5 per cent, of the carbon dioxide generated by the coal station.

The amount of carbon dioxide produced by nuclear power increases quite dramatically as lower grade ores are mined and extraction becomes more energy intensive, meaning that the use of speculative uranium reserves will produce as much carbon dioxide as coal. This is also a commentary on the economic unattractiveness of using low grade uranium ores.

This brings us on to a very big problem for nuclear power, and that is the distinctly finite nature of uranium resources.

The UK Atomic Energy Authority (UKAEA) said in its evidence to the House of Commons Select Committee on Energy's inquiry into the greenhouse effect that increasing nuclear's share of world electricity to 50 per cent by 2020 meant that all but speculative uranium resources would have been committed by that date. Even speculative resources would only last until 2100.[5]

The economics of extracting speculative resources would be prohibitive, quite apart from the fact that people living in places like Cornwall would be very unlikely to allow uranium mining and even less likely to want to work in such mines. As uranium became a depleted resource we would experience uranium crises. Oil crises are bad enough, but what of a uranium crisis?

If electricity consumption expands as a result of an expansion in demand for electrical services in developing nations, depletion crises would come all the more quickly. The oil crises show that economic and political events can trigger off crises long before resources are completely exhausted.

Of course the UKAEA's argument about uranium depletion was deployed to highlight its case for fast breeder reactors which can extend the life of uranium reserves through production of plutonium. Conventional 'thermal' reactors can only make use of the fissile uranium 235 isotope. This makes up less than 1 per cent of natural uranium which consists mostly of uranium 238. If the spent reactor fuel from thermal reactors is 'reprocessed', as at Sellafield, then at least some of the otherwise unused U–238 can be reclaimed along with some plutonium that is formed in the reactor. The UKAEA wants the government to support fast breeder research, which the government scrapped in 1988.

Fast breeder reactors, using fast as opposed to slowed down neutrons, can utilise the otherwise stable U–238 by turning it into plutonium, which is a very fissile material yielding nuclear energy. It can also be used in nuclear warheads.

Yet this opens another Pandora's box. Fast breeder technology, which has in any case hardly been made to work properly, magnifies several times the dangers of conventional nuclear power.

First, the chopping up and dissolution of nuclear waste for reprocessing generates a great volume of waste that could be much better managed without being reprocessed. It is no surprise that Sellafield's reprocessing facilities have been at the centre of concern over nuclear waste in the UK. Yet deployment of fast breeder technology would mean many more Sellafields. Today's nuclear waste problems would be multiplied many times over.

Second, fast breeder reactors are potentially far more unstable than conventional reactors in both chemical and nuclear terms. They use liquid sodium as a coolant, which reacts very easily and strongly. Unlike conventional reactors, fast breeders have the theoretical capability of producing a nuclear explosion because of the fissile nature of plutonium.

Third, a world electricity industry dominated by fast breeder nuclear reactors would produce a globe almost literally swimming in plutonium. It would be impossible to control or monitor the movements of plutonium. This would make nuclear proliferation an inevitable outcome. The possession of a fast breeder reactor would make it very easy for any government to make nuclear weapons under cover of producing electricity for civil purposes. An extremely frightening prospect also is that of the possibility of plutonium falling into the hands of terrorists. The security, never mind other, implications of the plutonium economy are horrifying enough. We should adopt an alternative, sustainable energy strategy.

All of this is on top of the mess that has already been made by the British nuclear industry.

The proposed privatisation of the electricity supply industry exposed the extremely uneconomic nature of the British nuclear power industry for all to see. Private investors were very unwilling to underwrite all the uncertainties and hazards associated with nuclear power.

Leaked cabinet papers, made public in October 1989, suggested that the cost of decommissioning nuclear power stations would push up the average cost of nuclear power to about 7 to 9 pence per kilowatt hour, which is about three times the cost of electricity generated from fossil fuels. The cost of nuclear power would push up electricity prices by at least fifteen per

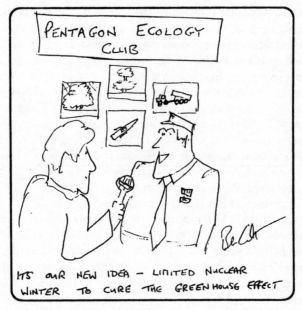

Figure 2.1: [Source: NATTA Newsletter 58, March/April 1989.]

cent.[6] These revelations were followed by a government announcement that the whole of the nuclear industry was to be taken out of the electricity sale and that the projected nuclear power station programme was to be curtailed.

Despite the gloss that has been put on these developments by the nuclear industry they will probably go down in history as events which spelt the end of nuclear power in Britain.

The issue of the cost of nuclear power is not just a technical one. Nuclear power is impossibly expensive precisely because of the difficulty of reconciling nuclear power with environmental protection which includes the safe disposal of nuclear waste and dismantling nuclear power stations which have come to the end of their lives. When the costs of these activities are taken fully into account it becomes abundantly clear that energy conservation and all but the most esoteric and underdeveloped forms of renewable energy are easily more cost effective than nuclear power as carbon dioxide abatement strategies.

The French nuclear power programme has, in recent years, been held up as an example of how nuclear power can supply around 70 per cent of national electricity at cheap prices. It certainly impressed Mrs Thatcher. Yet the state-run French nuclear programme has incurred very large debts, and the programme has yet to face up to the gargantuan problem of decommissioning power stations. When it does the French anti-nuclear lobby, which is already gathering strength, will make rapid progress.

The days when anti-nuclear protestors were easily dismissed, either as naive latter day Luddites or as unwitting agents of the KGB, are gone. Nowadays the prospect that defunct nuclear power stations will one day stand as ugly, expensive and ecologically tainted monuments to humanity's over-zealous belief in the triumph of science over nature cannot be quite so easily dismissed.

A vigorously pursued strategy of energy conservation allied with a determined effort to deploy renewable energy sources will enable us to phase out nuclear power in the UK and make large reductions in fossil fuel emissions. We would then not have to worry about the mounting quantities of nuclear waste, the expensive and complex decommissioning process that is now to be attempted on the retiring Magnox stations, and there would be no link between the UK's civil energy sector and the nuclear weapons programme. We would also be opting out of a strategy that leads us towards fast breeder reactors and the plutonium economy.

The 1988 and 1989 TUC policy of phasing out nuclear power within fifteen years is a moderate and realisable demand which should be explicitly pursued. It includes the demand that the construction of Sizewell B be terminated immediately. Otherwise, once the power station is turned on it will have to be subjected to the very expensive decommissioning process after it is shut down.

Political confidence in nuclear power's once proud claim of offering almost limitless quantities of energy has evaporated, but such enthusiasm still burns strongly in the hearts of enthusiasts for nuclear fusion. Advocates of greater spending on nuclear fusion say that if the technology could be developed, almost limitless energy supplies would be available with far less environmental impact than that associated with fission reactors.

The history of nuclear power with its early hope of almost zero-cost, problem-free energy suggests that we should be wary of such visions, especially in view of the colossal sums that would be needed to bring fusion into being, if it can be brought into being as a commercial proposition at all. Many believe that a fusion power station (and nobody has any idea what such a thing would look like) would have major environmental impacts resulting from its use of radioactive materials. In particular there could be dangerous releases of tritium and any fusion reactors would have to go through the same sort of expensive decommissioning process as fission reactors.[7]

What is remarkable is that the government spends more money on research into fusion, which has still not established itself as scientifically feasible,[8] than on all renewable sources, whose scientific feasibility is in most cases unquestioned. Tim Jackson has said that despite £20 billion having been spent into research into magnetic fusion over the past twenty-five years, not even the criteria for assessing the likely scientific feasibility have been established. He concludes an article in *Energy Policy* by saying:

> The decision maker is at present in no position to make any judgement at all on the wisdom of spending substantial sums of money on an enormous engineering project which may never work.[9]

Research and development into areas like wave power, geothermal energy and offshore wind is likely to yield considerably greater benefits in the medium term than research into fusion power.

The 'cold fusion' saga demonstrates how biased our social ideology is, in that we will eagerly accept high-science solutions while dismissing technology that acts in harmony with nature. The men in white coats with their test tubes are seen as a sort of modern priesthood. It seems that cold fusion probably does not exist at all, let alone that it can give us usable quantities of energy. It is strange that the cold fusion episode has been trumpeted as a reason for putting more money into fusion research. I would have thought the affair tends to discredit fusion rather than enhance its status! An explanation for this irrational faith in the power of nuclear science to produce magical solutions can be found not only in the self-interest of the large numbers of nuclear physicists but also in the very culture and education which has shaped our views throughout this century and especially since the end of the second world war.

High-temperature fusion could not be commercially viable for several decades. There is a very high probability that it will never be commercially viable and an even greater probability that it will not be cost-effective once the costs of environmental protection are taken into account. The assertion that such an energy option is going to be essential is dependent on accepting an extremely pessimistic assessment of the long term potentials of energy from natural sources. The levels of energy consumption that would force us to adopt fusion power (if it was a real possibility) would in all probability be unsustainable for a range of reasons.

A strategy which eschews the nuclear option can only be pursued alongside vigorous measures to reduce fossil fuel use. The most effective means of reducing fossil fuel use is through increasing energy efficiency. It is to this that I now turn.

3 Conserving Energy

The biggest problem we face in our efforts to increase the efficiency of energy conversion and use is that, in institutional, political and economic terms, the supply-side pressures for more energy production are much stronger than the demand-side pressures for higher energy efficiency.

We should be concerned with satisfying consumer demand for energy services such as lighting, heating, cooking, and refrigeration rather than with supplying more and more energy.

Supplying more energy is in institutional terms relatively easy because of the centralised nature of energy generation when compared to energy conservation, which requires many small actions by a disaggregated demand side of the market. Often energy conservation is seen as being peripheral to the central interests of the consumer. There is very little information about energy consumption of appliances, equipment or houses. Enormous quantities of economically viable energy conservation opportunities are not taken up by the market.

The market is by its very nature imbalanced, and environmentalist objectives can only be fully achieved by intervention through regulation, tax incentives and penalties, grants and subsidies, and decentralised, flexible forms of public ownership. We also need to mobilise both political and consumer pressure.

However, such calls for increased intervention to achieve the aim of sustainable energy policy should not be confused with rigid centralised types of planning. Local control and flexibility are essential if the needs of the environment and consumers are to be given priority over the preferences of bureaucrats and producer interest groups.

Although the UK's Energy Efficiency Office has, since its establishment in 1983, achieved some energy savings in the industrial sector, its efforts have been stunted by several factors. These include inadequate finance, a role which relegates it to providing information for the market rather than active intervention in it, and subordination to a department whose main interest group 'clients' are concerned with growth in energy production rather than improving energy efficiency.

The government's cynical attitude to energy conservation was typified by a statement made by Junior Energy Minister Michael Spicer, who was trying to fend off mounting criticism of the government's lack of attention to energy conservation in the Electricity Privatisation Bill. He said:

> It is unacceptable just to tell people to turn the lights out and the fires and the kettles. This, if they are honest, is what those who argue for conservation as the primary means of solving the greenhouse effect really mean.[1]

Contrary to what Michael Spicer says, a radical programme of energy conservation does not involve reductions in living standards. Energy conservation or, more precisely, improving energy efficiency involves using less energy to produce a given amount of goods or services. Energy efficiency can be improved either by cutting out wastage in energy conversion (this applies mostly to electricity production) or by reducing energy demand by using less energy for a given end.

It is estimated that before 1973 annual gains in energy efficiency ran at around 1 per cent, with the rate increasing to nearer 2 per cent in the aftermaths of the two big oil price rises in the 1970s. As oil prices came down in the second part of the 1980s interest in energy efficiency declined.

Conservationists argue that there is so much wastage that the rates of energy efficiency improvement could be massively increased over the next couple of decades. Some countries, like Denmark and Japan, were heavily dependent on oil imports because they had few indigenous energy sources. They were especially threatened by the oil price rises. They have had considerable success in their energy conservation programmes, although a large part of their policies was oriented towards finding substitutes for oil, rather than conservation *per se*. How-

ever, with falling oil prices the Japanese have become less worried and their oil consumption has once more started to increase.

In other places energy conservation programmes have been
half-hearted or practically non-existent. Greens argue that the
threat of the greenhouse effect and mounting green political
pressure will provide increasing motivation for conservationist
strategies. But what, in practical terms, do such strategies
involve?

First I shall deal with the deployment of combined heat and
power to reduce conversion losses and then I shall look at how
the end-use efficiency of energy could be improved.

COMBINED HEAT AND POWER

The biggest single amount of energy wastage occurs in the conversion of fossil fuels into electricity. Little more than a third
of the energy input is converted into electricity, the rest being
discarded mainly in the form of hot flue gases.

Much of the waste heat could be used to provide space heating
and hot water. This system is called combined heat and power
(CHP), or co-generation. It can provide heat for district heating
networks that serve homes, offices and businesses as a conserved
by-product of electricity generation. The district heating systems
can at first be provided with heat from central boilers and later
from power stations which also produce electricity.

Combined heat and power can be used in industry to provide
both electricity and heat at the same time. Hospitals and other
self-contained institutions can provide their own heat and electricity. Micro-CHP systems are even being developed that can
supply heat and power for individual houses.

A power station integrated with a CHP system can produce
the same amount of energy as a conventional station, using just
half the quantity of fossil fuel. This increases energy efficiency
from around 35 per cent to up to 70 per cent. Newer breeds of,
for example, combined cycle gas turbines could push efficiency
levels even higher.

Combined heat and power use is expanding in many European
countries. In Denmark the potential of CHP/district heating is

being realised through the promotion of small CHP units in places like hospitals and factories and by laying down regulations saying that in urban areas local authorities have the power to insist that people join in CHP and district heating schemes rather than use natural gas. By 1985 Denmark had 40 per cent of its total heating requirement supplied by district heating, and half of this was supplied by CHP/district heating. These proportions are still increasing at a rapid pace.

In many parts of Scandinavia small combined heat and power plants supply housing estates and apartment blocks. In West Germany there is a considerable amount of CHP/district heating. Electricity from industrial CHP provides around 15 per cent of the country's electricity supply.

Recent UK government reports have highlighted the cost-effectiveness of industrial CHP and small CHP in general. In 1984 the Atkins Report said there was a potential of 7GW of electricity CHP capacity. A recent Friends of the Earth Memorandum commented that each GWe of coal fired CHP would reduce overall carbon dioxide emissions by 3Mt/annum and each GWe of gas CHP would reduce overall emissions by around 6Mt/annum.[2]

Yet there is little district heating in this country and an even smaller amount of community based CHP. Despite increasing interest in CHP and even provision for it in the 1983 Energy Act there seems little chance of a CHP programme of Danish dimensions starting in this country in the near future.

British Gas, who do not want competition from district heating (which can be piped just as easily as gas) has been an important obstacle to CHP developments in the UK. Yet the existence of gas heating does not limit the potential for installing CHP/district heating systems. In fact the existence of gas central heating units means that the costs of implementing CHP/district heating systems can be reduced because the central heating systems can be 'plugged in' to the district heating networks.

The amount of industrial co-generation in the UK has actually declined since the 1970s despite industrially based CHP being among the most cost effective carbon dioxide abatement strategies. A big factor in the decline of industrial co-generation in the UK and the failure of local authorities to develop community CHP schemes is the low tariffs that have been paid to co-generation schemes for electricity sold to the grid. It is much cheaper for an established generating organisation like the CEGB to supply more electricity from its existing capacity than it is for a new entrant to the market such as an industrial co-generator or an independent electricity producer of whatever sort, because the independent has to pay the capital costs of the new capacity.

The post-privatisation arrangements will not improve the situation as the already established generating companies, the duopoly consisting of PowerGen and National Power, can use their existing position to underbid independents in the negotiations with the area electricity distribution companies. On top of this the area distribution companies find it administratively simpler to award contracts to a couple of large generators than to many small independents. Independents are in any case severely constrained by the fact that the duopoly control, and already have planning permission to cover, the best sites for power stations.

In the USA there is legislation requiring that co-generators be paid good rates for their electricity, on the long run avoided cost principle. This is the Public Utility Regulatory Policies Act (PURPA) which made the utilities which bought electricity from independents pay them the cost the utilities would have incurred had they had to build new generating capacity to supply the electricity.

This has benefited the fast growing co-generation sector in California in particular, although in the last couple of years the electricity establishment has managed to gain the removal of some of the incentives given to independent electricity producers. This country desperately needs PURPA-type legislation and regulation to ensure that co-generators and other independents receive a reasonable price for power that is sold to the grid.

The lack of CHP in the UK has a lot to do with the centralised nature of our electricity system. This has meant that planners have gone for 'efficient' large power stations usually sited away from potential district heating customers, despite the fact that the community would be given a far less wasteful service through building small power stations providing heat to local communities, businesses and public institutions.

Nigel Lucas, a widely respected observer of European energy politics, looked at the development of schemes involving the efficient planning of electricity supply along with heating and gas in West Germany, and commented:

> The thrust for this kind of innovation comes from smaller municipal utilities whose primary vision of the world is defined by the economic geography of a town rather than by the exigencies of a national power system.[3]

Lucas also commented that the reasons why CHP/district heating has been much more successful in Denmark than the UK have had a lot to do with the fact that in Denmark local government is much more involved in energy provision than in the UK, and that the Danes have a much stronger co-operative tradition.

Practical experience demonstrates the efficacy of decentralised forms of organisation in the pursuit of energy conservation. The electricity supply industry badly needs restructuring on a decentralised basis with considerable local government involvement.

It is highly unlikely that a Conservative government will consider such a reform. However, if the Conservatives lose power, the municipalisation of the electricity supply industry should be high on the agenda of a new government. I shall discuss this further when I come to consider institutional changes later in this book. But whatever the exact nature of such institutional changes, they must operate in the context of a national plan for energy conservation, implemented by local bodies with regard to local needs. Such a strategy should involve institutions which should, as in Denmark, have the power to earmark entire areas solely for district heating.

Emphasis must be placed on developing district heating systems in order to provide a heatload for CHP stations which could be built either at the same time or later.

Besides municipalising the electricity supply industry an important measure would be to create a National Heat Board which could co-ordinate the development of local district heating and then CHP schemes. The Heat Board should have access to large quantities of finance derived from energy taxation which it could use to provide investment for schemes worked out by the municipal authorities. An annual investment of around £800 million could ensure that within a fifteen year period the majority of houses in the UK were supplied with district heating which could be linked to either city-wide or small CHP schemes.

Public financing of CHP/district heating is necessary because of the difficulty faced by municipal bodies in trying to raise funds from the market to develop heat and power schemes that have a long payback period. British banks are notoriously short term in their attitudes. Nevertheless provided investment finance is available on reasonable terms there should be powerful incentives to local bodies to develop CHP/district heating schemes. In this way councils can improve housing services, many jobs can be created, and the municipal bodies who run the schemes will derive a steady income from the investments after the schemes have been started. Grants should be given for small CHP in the public sector, and planning law should be altered so that all large developments are assessed for CHP.

The prospects for CHP could have been brightened if the government, during the debates on electricity privatisation, had allowed heat produced by CHP to count as part of the 20 per cent 'non-fossil' fraction of electricity supply (designed to protect nuclear power from extinction) that Area Boards have to accept.

In general, we must establish a situation where no fossil fuel generating plant is built unless its wastage of energy is cut down to a minimum. This means small, industrial and community oriented CHP stations rather than remote gigawatt dinosaurs.

When we have arrived at this position we shall have achieved a considerable reduction in energy wastage resulting from energy conversion. However, this is only part of the story as far as energy saving is concerned. Immense savings can be gained by more effective use of delivered energy. I shall look at how such savings can be achieved first in the electricity sector and then in other areas.

REDUCING THE DEMAND FOR ELECTRICITY

Electricity demand could be massively reduced if energy efficiency policies were energetically pursued.

As can be seen in Table 3.1, the energy consumption of appliances like lights, fridges, washing machines and even TVs could be massively reduced if the most energy efficient models were bought, and the cost of such choices would be much less than the cost of building new power stations.

Table 3.1: Electricity consumption of electrical appliances

Appliance Electricity Consumption (kwh/year)

	UK Stock	Best Available Technology
Refrigerator/freezer (0.5 m³)	1,100	75–180
Freezer (0.25 m³)	1,000	80–180
Refrigerator (frost-free, 0.2m³)	450	30–80
Washing machine	400	40–210
Dishwasher	500	50–240
Clothes Dryer	520	10–90
Colour TV	340	70

Source: Memorandum by Friends of the Earth to the House of Lords European Communities Sub-Committee B for its enquiry into 'Efficiency of Electricity Use'. *London, FOE, 1989.*

Note: the figures in the 'best available technology' column represent prototype models and best models available on the world market. 'UK stock' means the average consumption of models in use.

A comprehensive and easily understandable system of energy labelling should be made compulsory so that consumers can see how much electricity a given appliance is going to use and can compare such usage with other models of the same appliance.

Setting minimum standards of electrical efficiency for the most common electrical appliances is an even more important measure, and would result in enormous savings given the big disparity in energy efficiencies of different models.

In 1987 the US Congress approved legislation that will considerably improve the efficiency of electrical appliances. Under the new laws the large majority of appliances in use in 1985 become illegal in 1990 or 1992 because they do not reach the required efficiency standards. By 2000 this legislation is likely to save an electricity output equivalent to that of about twenty-one large power stations.

In the UK Friends of the Earth have proposed that minimum standards of electrical efficiency be set so that by 1993 all appliances on sale are at least as efficient as the ten per cent most efficient appliances now available. In the case of a fridge with a volume of $0.15m^3$, the average efficiency of models on sale in 1987–89 was 270 KWh per annum. Under Friends of the Earth's proposal the standard would be 170 KWh p.a., although the best available in Europe used only 80 KWh p.a. (for a $0.2m^3$ fridge) and a prototype exists which used just 40 KWh p.a.[4]

The UK government should implement the sort of standards suggested by Friends of the Earth as soon as possible. Some might argue that we should wait for action at a European Community level so that British industry will be better protected. Such an argument is shortsighted. Action at a European Community level is indeed essential, but given that it is also inevitable, British industry will be all the better able to cope with international competition if it has first learned to adapt to efficiency standards on a UK basis.

Efficiency standards should be regularly upgraded so that after a few years the standards are put up to the efficiency levels achieved by the present range of 'state of the art' models. Thereafter efficiency standards should be strengthened to keep pace with technical improvements. The Harwell-based Energy Technical Support Unit should be given the brief of monitoring efficiency improvements.

In the above-mentioned memorandum to a House of Lords Select Committee, written by David Olivier for Friends of the Earth, it was stated that if demand side conservation policies were fully applied, current levels of electrical services could be provided using only 30 per cent of present levels of electricity consumption. This would reduce the UK's peak electricity demand from 50GW to 15GW. This 70 per cent reduction would be achieved by using the most efficient electrical appliances available on the market and by replacing electric space and water heating by district heating from combined heat and power systems.

Because the demand for electrical services is constantly increasing, with larger numbers of computers, video cassette recorders, freezers and other electrical appliances being operated, the actual reduction in electricity demand will be, in the short term, rather less than 70 per cent. Nor is it economic to implement all the technically possible energy saving measures at once, because it is often uneconomic to replace an inefficient electrical appliance or piece of machinery much before the end of its normal operating lifetime.

However, according to Olivier, the energy efficiency of the best available technology is improving by 4 per cent per year, much faster than the average rate of UK economic growth. Massive cuts in electricity consumption seem possible, even if new electricity uses are found (such as powering cars from renewable energy sources).

If we assume economic growth to be 2.2 per cent per annum (close to the average for the 1970s and 1980s), assume the increase in demand for electrical services to be roughly the same, and assume a realistically achievable timetable for successively tightening electrical efficiency standards, then within a twenty year period we can realistically achieve a reduction in electricity demand of between 30 and 40 per cent.

This target depends on the replacement of 80–90 per cent of plant and appliances in current use within the twenty year period. It also depends on the replacement of at least four-fifths of electric space and water heating by CHP-supplied district heating. This 30 to 40 per cent reduction could only be achieved in the context of vigorous and urgent action to implement energy efficiency measures.

Given that the Swedish State Power Board is planning to reduce electricity consumption by between 14 and 32 per cent by 2010, such projections would not be entirely without precedent.

If we look towards a longer timescale, the reductions could be larger. After all Amory Lovins and his colleagues have designed buildings and pinpointed technology that will operate on energy levels as low as a tenth or less of present requirements. On the other hand we shall have to live with much of the present building stock (however extensively retrofitted) for many decades to come, and it is difficult to predict with any certainty the likely future shape or size of growth in demand for electrical services. With sufficient political will it is conceivable that over the next 35 years electricity demand could be reduced by over 50 per cent of present levels.

However such projections rely on very high and sustained gains in energy efficiency that could only be achieved in a context where energy and resource efficiency is at the very top of the political and social agenda. Today it still ranks well down the list, despite the high-sounding rhetoric that gushes forth from our political leaders.

These types of projection are very radical compared to the projections of the CEGB, who in a submission to the Hinkley C nuclear power station inquiry stated that by 2040 peak electricity demand will have increased by some 60 per cent. The CEGB claimed to have taken into account energy efficiency improvements, but they assume that only some of the economically achievable efficiency opportunities are taken up. Maximum take-up of energy efficiency opportunities will only be achieved by implementing the right policies.

Although the need for legislation and government intervention is of paramount importance, changes in consumer tastes and consumer purchasing pressure in the direction of environmentally sustainable practices are also important elements of any conservationist strategy.

The most (literally) visible aspect of any green campaign on electrical efficiency would be in persuading people to switch to low energy fluorescent light bulbs. They fit in all but the smallest standard light fittings (some newer ones even in small table lamps) and are much cheaper in the long run, even if the fluorescent bulbs are more expensive to buy than conventional tungsten ones.

For example a Wotan Dulux EL 25 watt bulb will give out an equivalent amount of light to a standard 100 watt light bulb, but it uses 75 per cent less electricity. It is one of the more expensive fluorescent models, having a capital cost of £18, at

1989 prices. Nevertheless when the running costs of standard tungsten light bulbs are also taken into account, savings of around 40 per cent in total bills will be achieved by using fluorescent bulbs. Rumours that much of this advantage is lost because fluorescent bulbs consume a great deal of power when being switched on are simply false.

Older types of fluorescent bulbs like the Phillips SL series are cheaper at £10 to £11 (1989 prices), although these may give headaches to a very small proportion of people, a problem that the newer models avoid because of their built-in electronic ballasts.

It is surprising that no electrical store (at the time of writing) has cottoned on to the commercial possibilities of launching a green consumer campaign to sell fluorescent bulbs. It would certainly save consumers a lot of money. A survey in *Which?* magazine suggested that many households could save over £100 a year by switching to fluorescent lights.[5]

I do not wish to exaggerate the importance of green consumer campaigns. After all, energy efficiency is all too often regarded as being one of the minor criteria in model selection, although proper energy labelling and greater consumer awareness will make a difference. Nevertheless, a consumer campaign in the area of domestic lighting would be extremely useful. If all domestic consumers changed to using the newest types of fluorescent bulbs the saving would amount to well over the output of a large power station.

Many consumers will be unwilling to pay the relatively high cost of a fluorescent bulb whatever the savings in the long run. But, as I suggest later, electricity companies could actually reduce their costs by subsidising consumers to buy low energy light bulbs that will reduce demand sufficient to avoid the need of building costly extra generating capacity.

Another area of domestic energy saving that should be easily understandable is washing machines. Hot-filled machines are usually more efficient in energy terms than cold-fill ones, especially if the household heating system is gas fired.

Large savings in lighting costs could be achieved in the commercial and industrial sectors by using the most energy efficient fluorescent lights and designing buildings to make maximum use of daylight.

A fast expanding use of electricity is in air conditioning in public and commercial buildings. Yet the systems we are deploying are so inefficient that they use more electricity than up-to-date systems used in Jamaica. In fact there should be little call for air conditioning in this country. David Olivier has commented:

> The need for refrigerating buildings in the southern UK, whose peak summer temperatures and relative humidities are among the lowest in industrial countries, must be seriously questioned. Denmark's summer temperatures match southern England's, but the case for this use of electricity was so weak that it prohibited it 10 years ago . . . [6]

Energy conscious building designs can provide a substitute for air conditioning by flushing buildings with cool air at night making them cooler by day.

It is much more difficult to set standards for industrial electrical equipment than for domestic machines since while the latter are standardised mass-produced items, the former are often plant-specific, dedicated to a particular purpose. Here a range of tactics are appropriate including energy taxation, tax incentives for energy efficiency purposes and regulation through Energy Efficiency Inspectors. I shall look at these in more detail later.

In general, this country's energy practices are much more wasteful than those of our European competitors. For example, German freezers use less than a third of the electricity that UK models of a similar size consume. Prototype Danish freezers use less than a sixth that of average UK freezers.

In Scandinavia the idea of reducing energy demand has much greater credibility than in the UK. Sweden has decided to phase out nuclear power, which provides more than 50 per cent of its electricity. It is embarking on an ambitious programme of energy efficiency and, as we saw earlier, the Swedish State Power Board is planning large reductions in electricity demand.

By contrast in the spring of 1989 the CEGB told MPs that it planned to increase carbon dioxide emissions by 25 per cent

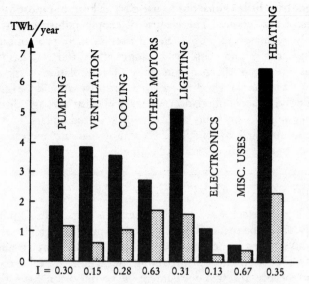

Figure 3.1: Potentials for electricity conservation. [Source: Nils I Meyer and Jørgen S Nørgård, Planning Implications of Electricity Conservation: The Case of Denmark, in T. B. Johansson, B. Bodlund & R. H Williams (eds.) Electricity. Efficient End-Use and New Generation Technologies, and Their Planning Implications. Lund University Press & Chartwell-Bratt, 1989.]

Potential for electricity conservation in Denmark. Dark columns indicate present electricity consumption. Grey columns indicate possible reduced consumption with known technology and same energy service. The ratio between the reduced consumption and the present consumption is denoted electricity intensity index, I. Studies of conservation potential in the UK show very similar results.

over the following fifteen years and 60 per cent over the following fifty years.

The CEGB's unrestrained zeal for electricity production has also tied up part of the space and water heating markets in domestic, industrial and commercial sectors, despite the fact that electricity heating is far less efficient than gas or district heating in its use of primary energy.

Admittedly some people in tower blocks or areas not piped

for gas have little choice but to use electric heat, but most others do have that choice. The electricity supply industry must be closely regulated to stop such excesses as their promotion of storage heaters, and people who cannot afford to install gas fires should be given 100 per cent grants for insulation work and the installation of gas fires. Urgent priority should be given to supplying accommodation blocks with heat through district heating schemes probably at first using gas-fired boilers. District heating supplied by small CHP stations should increasingly replace both electrical and gas heating.

LEAST COST PLANNING

Whether the electricity supply industry is in private or public hands it must be required by law to adopt practices which ensure that investment in new generating capacity does not go ahead before the possibilities of providing the same electrical services more cheaply through investment in conservation have been exhausted.

In many parts of the USA the pricing and investment policies of electricity utilities are subjected to public scrutiny to ensure that conservation policies have been properly applied. This is the 'least cost' planning system that is used in a majority of American states, although the actual degree of regulation varies. The regulatory bodies are called Public Utility Commissions.

Least cost planning must be adopted by the British electricity industry. American experience has demonstrated that when power generation and distribution companies subsidise investment in energy efficiency they can become more cost effective since the cost of energy saving measures is, up to a point, smaller than the cost of building new power stations. Electricity utilities use conservation supply curves to estimate the costs of supplying different amounts of energy conservation, sometimes described as 'negawatts'. Figure 3.2 shows an example of a conservation supply curve.

In the USA many utilities spend a great deal of time and effort offering advice and finance to electricity consumers so that they can use electricity – and energy in general – more efficiently.

For example, the Tennessee Valley Authority gives help to the domestic sector by offering free home energy surveys, interest-free loans for home insulation and financial assistance for the installation of energy saving heat pumps, and for building energy efficient new homes. Loans of up to $300,000 per customer have been available in the commercial and industrial sector for money-saving investments and the Authority's engineering staff and industrial representatives give a great deal of advice to businesses. Its 1987 energy services report said that in-depth surveys had been conducted with 2000 residential consumers to hear their views and assess their needs. Special assistance has been given to low-income households through outreach programs.[7]

Some utilities will subsidise investment in energy efficiency by financing the replacement of old inefficient appliances like refrigerators with newer, more efficient ones.

The nature of the regulatory bodies, the Public Utility Commissions, varies. California's Public Utility Commission system is among the most advanced. The most progressive Commissions allow all interested groups to make submissions, and have the function of carefully examining and if necessary demanding the alteration of the electric company's investment, pricing and demand management policies so that these policies fit in with least cost criteria.

A regulatory system that would ensure the application of least cost integrated planning techniques should be adopted in the UK. Under electricity privatisation, the Director-General of Electricity does not have the power to regulate the electricity supply industry according to least cost criteria, and there is certainly no mechanism for involving the public in checking the wisdom of investment and pricing decisions. If, as I recommend later, the industry is municipalised, local or regional utility commissions should be established as well as a national body.

The electricity distribution utilities (the Area Electricity Boards under privatisation) should be allowed to include the costs of subsidising energy conservation in their prices. Electricity prices may increase to pay for investment in conservation, but consumers will gain much more than they lose since a great

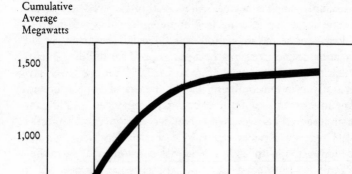

Cumulative
Average
Megawatts

Figure 3.2: A conservation supply curve over a 20 year period. [Source: Ian Brown, 'Least Cost Integrated Planning' evidence to Hinkley 'C' Enquiry, Hinkley, Consortium of Opposing Local Authorities, 1988.]

deal less electricity will be consumed for the same output of electrical services.

It is relevant at this juncture to make the point that even if energy conservation is deployed up to its maximum economic potential, we still need *some* new generating capacity.

Figure 3.2 shows a conservation supply curve drawn up by the Pacific Northwest Company to show the technical conservation potential from its commercial sector. The supply curve compares the amount of conservation that can be supplied at different prices over, in this case, a twenty year period.

Demand for new generating capacity appears to arise not only because of increasing demand for electrical services, but also because old power stations come to the end of their lives and cost increasingly more to maintain, making it cheaper to replace them with newer, more efficient stations. This fact, together with a policy of phasing out nuclear power, will make the task of investing in renewable electricity generating capacity an urgent and important priority which goes hand in hand with strong measures to reduce electricity demand.

Renewable sources should form the majority of new generating capacity with the balance being provided by small-scale, CHP linked fossil fuel plant. I shall comment further on the supply side options in Chapter Four.

Such a strategy which emphasises both energy conservation and renewable energy sources is not being taken seriously by the present Department of Energy.

For example, the government refused to accept amendments to the Electricity Privatisation Bill made by the House of Lords which sought to make sure the electricity supply industry was regulated according to least cost criteria. The amendments, which sought to give the Director-General of the electricity industry powers to vet investment and pricing policies to make sure that energy conservation strategies had been properly applied, were rejected. The only concession the group of Tory rebels managed to extract was a woolly statement in favour of conservation which lacked any means of enforcement.

Nevertheless there are signs that some parts of the message about energy conservation are seeping through to some sections of the industry. PowerGen, the smaller element of the generating duopoly, claims that it will make a determined effort to improve investment in energy efficiency and has even made a few noises about encouraging alternative fuels. The East Midlands Electricity Board called in US energy conservation guru Amory Lovins to advise them how they might increase energy efficiency after privatisation.

However, these are only chinks of light in a darkened room. As I have already noted, prospects for energy conservation in general, including combined heat and power, would be considerably advanced if electricity and heat provision were integrated and run by locally accountable energy utilities. I shall discuss this later when I come to consider the political means of implementing sustainable energy policies.

I shall now turn to non-electricity energy use in buildings and transport which mainly involves gas heating and fuel.

BUILDINGS

Over a third of total UK carbon dioxide emissions result from space or water heating and the bulk of this is from space heating.

The demand for space heating could be dramatically reduced if Scandinavian standards of thermal efficiency were incorporated into building regulations. Houses in cold countries like Sweden are built with much better wall, roof, floor, door and window insulation than British houses for little extra cost. Very little heat is required to keep a Swedish or Canadian house up to an ambient temperature of around 21°C. By comparison British houses are thermal sieves and a house built to 1988 UK efficiency standards is only up to the level of a Swedish house built in 1940.

Building regulations are being altered to take minimum thermal efficiency standards from a wall U value of 0.6 W/m²/°C to 0.45 W/m²/°C. We could take this much further. Swedish standards stand at 0.15 W/m²/°C. We should upgrade our standards to 0.3 immediately, meet present Swedish levels by 1995 and bring wall U value standards to about 0.11 by the year 2000.

British builders tend to complain that super-insulated buildings produce condensation problems. Others point out that the lack of circulating air can lead to the easier spread of diseases. In some areas a build-up of radon gas can cause cancer. Such problems can be easily avoided by using air management systems which ensure a constant airflow while at the same time retaining heat through the use of heat exchangers. They also have the added 'comfort' value of removing unwanted household smells.

Such systems use only a small amount of electricity. In this country Creda market a model that runs on 100 watts, although this is considerably more than models available in Sweden that use only 30 to 40 watts, little more than an energy efficient lightbulb. Building regulations should stipulate that efficient air management systems are installed when new houses are built.

In addition to strengthening building regulations, minimum standards of efficiency for gas boilers should be introduced to ensure that the more efficient gas condensing boilers are used.

A major training programme for builders will have to be launched and more building inspectors appointed as the drive for energy efficiency in buildings gathers pace.

Various studies show how people can both be much warmer and consume far less energy in energy efficient houses. Studies of the Pennylands housing project in Milton Keynes illustrated how inhabitants cut heating bills by almost half.[8]

In addition to better insulation, houses can use passive solar energy if they include south facing windows and perhaps conservatories.

A great deal can be done to reduce the energy consumption of existing housing stock. According to the Association for the Conservation of Energy (ACE) a major programme of domestic energy conservation could create between 67,000 and 155,000 jobs by the end of a 10 year period after taking account of job losses in the energy supply industries.[9] These jobs would involve insulation work on lofts and cavity walls, draughtstripping and double glazing. Around 70 per cent of UK dwellings are still not insulated up to even basic standards.

ACE advocated giving 75 per cent grants to consumers for energy conservation work. Given the need to ensure the maximisation of take-up the grants should be associated with low interest loans to 'top up' the grant. Low income households should receive 100 per cent grants.

In addition to this minimum programme there should be more extensive retrofitting of old buildings including much better insulated floors, doors, walls and roofs. Indeed such retrofitting should form an essential second stage of a domestic energy conservation programme. Such an ongoing programme would, if vigorously pursued, demand public expenditure of at least £1,000 million a year continuing into the indefinite future.

Even this sum, as large as it appears, is small compared to the potential work that could be cost-effectively done. A South East

Economic Development Strategy study concluded that a basic loft, draughtstripping and cavity wall insulation programme alone covering just housing stock in Brighton and Harlow would cost £1,380 million. Yet such a programme would produce sufficient savings to pay for itself in only 4.3 years. The loft insulation part of the programme would pay for itself through reduced bills in just 2.5 years.[10]

The success and take-up of such a scheme would depend on several factors, not least the priority which the government attached to the programme. Energy efficiency standards should be set for existing public buildings and public housing which together constitute around half the country's total building stock. Central and local government should do energy audits on their building stock and arrange for insulation to be done and paid for through the domestic conservation programme or through capital funds given to local authorities and central government agencies to retrofit public buildings. Energy utility companies should advertise the programme on the bills (printed on 100 per cent recycled paper) they send to consumers and should invest heavily in energy efficiency to insulate homes and replace inefficient appliances with more efficient ones.

An important boost would be given to energy conservation if legislation was enacted stipulating that before the sale of a house is completed, the prospective owners are furnished with an account of the property's energy efficiency levels, calculated according to a recognised index. This would require energy audits to be completed which would enforce work to be done to improve insulation standards. Regrettably, efforts at European Community level to legislate for a mandatory system of energy labelling for buildings have been stalled, with the UK government being among those resisting the idea. Meanwhile, the Milton Keynes based National Energy Foundation has developed a simple system for assessing the energy efficiency of buildings using a 0 to 10 rating, 10 being the most energy efficient. A house built to meet the current building regulations has a rating of 5.

Insulation work would be done by local companies. Given sufficient promotion and educational work by local authorities, government and co-operative development agencies, many of these companies could be worker co-operatives.

Many people, including those connected with the energy supply industries, deride the idea that better insulation of old houses can reduce energy demand. It is certainly the case that some of the energy saving potential of conservation disappears as consumers opt for greater warmth. This is particularly the case with low income households.

On the one hand this is hardly an argument against a vigorous conservation programme since it benefits the consumer. On the other hand many studies, as well as Scandinavian experience, indicate that better insulation does save very large amounts of energy besides providing more comfort.

According to calculations published by David Olivier and others in the study *Energy Efficient Futures*[11] the nation's domestic heating consumption would be cut by two-thirds if the tighter building regulations and the energy conservation programme I advocate were put into practice. This saving would be on the basis of almost universal central heating providing room temperatures of 21°C. The bulk of this heating would be provided by district heating schemes.

In the past few years many councils have developed energy management schemes. In Birmingham it is hoped to save 10 per cent of the Corporation's energy bill in five years in a programme that started in 1987. Dorset County Council have achieved even better results, and reduced energy consumption by 23 per cent saving around £1 million in energy bills.

Large savings in energy consumption can be made simply by using electronic building energy management systems. Some local authorities and businesses are making good use of such systems, but their use is far from universal in commerce, industry and especially government departments.

Unfortunately only a small fraction of the economically feasible energy savings are being made by local authorities at present. People must agitate at a local level for greater action to achieve energy efficiency and at a national level the government should set efficiency standards to force the local authorities to take action. For example, when renovation work is done, energy efficiency improvements must be made. However, local authorities are discouraged from spending on investment in energy conservation which has a payback period longer than five years because the councils may not recoup the cost of borrowing money on the market. This underlines the need for capital grants to be made available to local authorities by the government.

One thing that all councils can do regardless of government policy is to assist the formation of 'fuelsavers' or 'energy enterprise' schemes and businesses which can help low income households pay for insulation work through the money they save from paying reduced energy bills. The Birmingham based Community Energy Research has been attempting to achieve this. The Housing Renovation Grants Scheme should be altered to include a basic level of energy efficiency as part of the 'fitness standard'. Grants would thus have to be given for work involving insulation, heating controls and so on.

Besides being given free home insulation, low income households should be given better treatment by the energy utilities. Rather than cutting off supplies, utilities should have to seek payment of unpaid bills through the courts.

An effective energy conservation programme and an improved all round energy service to the community can be best provided if a network of energy advice services are built up.

PAYING FOR CONSERVATION

During this chapter I have advocated that public funds provide massive investment in district heating and CHP and in public building and domestic energy conservation programmes. This investment should be paid for through energy taxation. This includes 'carbon' taxes and 'nuclear' taxes levied to encourage energy efficiency and fuel switching to renewables. Massive sums could be raised by the simple device of charging VAT on energy consumption. We should bear in mind that energy prices have fallen, in real terms, by 10 per cent between 1983 and 1988. The funds raised out of taxes on energy could contribute to an Environmental Protection Fund.

It might be argued that energy conservation should be funded by direct taxation, but the problem with this is that conservation will then be competing for scarce funds with spending on areas like education and health. I shall discuss such arguments later when looking at the issue of energy taxation in greater detail. But whatever system is used to finance the investment, consumers will gain much more than they lose.

However, the government feels that consumers will pay for conservation themselves once they have been given the right information. They ignore the fact that the energy supply industry allows itself much longer payback periods than can be afforded by consumers. Nor will many consumers bother to invest in energy conservation if there is a reasonable chance of them moving within a few years.

Despite the government's vocal concern about the greenhouse effect, spending on insulation grants has been cut back and local conservation programmes severely stunted by the scrapping of the Community Programme and its replacement by the so-called Employment Training Initiative.

TRANSPORT

The two most energy efficient and, in general terms, most environmentally benign forms of transport are walking and cycling. Transport policy should be geared to favour these modes of transport before others.

Of course this does not mean we should stop travelling. Nevertheless we must make major efforts to shift both passenger and freight transportation onto public transport. Buses and trains are much more energy efficient than private motor cars. Public transport should be heavily subsidised to provide a convenient and cheap alternative to cars.

Regulations and taxation policy should be aimed at improving the fuel efficiency of motor vehicles and vehicles should in general be taxed so that the price of travel reflects the ecological and social damage caused.

Some of the considerable energy efficiency lead of trains over cars is taken away because electricity, upon which trains are increasingly run, is itself wasteful by virtue of conversion losses in electricity generation.

Two developments should reduce the carbon dioxide emissions caused by electric rail transport. First, combined heat and power systems will reduce the wastefulness of electricity generation. Secondly, as a higher proportion of electrical generation is provided by renewable sources, so its associated carbon dioxide emissions will be reduced.

Transport by private motor cars is an ecological disaster area. Now that cars are increasingly being run on lead-free petrol and catalytic converters are being introduced, petrol companies and others are proclaiming the advent of 'green cars'. This is nonsense. The only green car is a bicycle.

Whereas in the UK carbon dioxide emissions from industry have fallen dramatically since the 1970s, and emissions from other sectors have been fairly constant, carbon dioxide emissions from road transport have been increasing at a rapid rate. Between 1977 and 1987 they increased by over a third and now make up around 16 per cent of all the UK's carbon production.

There has been considerable public disquiet about the 1989 white paper *Roads for Prosperity*[12] issued by the Department of Transport, which advocated investment in road building costing £6,600 million on the basis of a projected increase in road use of between 83 and 142 per cent by 2025. People are already fed up with the environmental impact of roads which are rapidly destroying our towns, cities and countryside as they plough up everything in their path and reshape society in various undesirable ways. These facts, added to the road accident casualties, noise and smog produced by cars are enough to justify a 180 degree turnaround in transport policy priorities, towards very much greater support to bicycles, buses and trains. The impact of ever increasing car use on global warming makes this doubly necessary. Yet the need to improve the energy efficiency of cars was completely ignored by the Department of Transport in their white paper.

A crucially important measure would be the setting of stringent minimum fuel standards for vehicles. This would be best done at the level of the European Community, although there should be no excuse for not implementing fuel efficiency standards now at a UK level. There are many new models, either prototypes or already on sale, that have very high fuel efficiencies. At present the average fuel economy for new cars stands at around 35 miles per gallon in Japan and Europe and around 30 miles per gallon in the UK. Some prototypes run on up to 145 miles per gallon at 56 mph. Austin Rover claim a 100 miles per gallon for their Montego turbo diesel, for example.

Deborah Bleviss, whose book *The New Oil Crisis and Fuel Economy Technologies*[13] describes ways of making cars and trucks more fuel efficient, believes that a determined political effort could double average fuel efficiencies over a 10 year period. Ultra-lean burn engines, reducing the weight of vehicles by using materials like ceramics and aluminium instead of steel, improved electronic transmissions, better aerodynamics and energy storage innovations can increase fuel economy tremendously.

Cars running on diesel tend to be more efficient than petrol driven models. Diesel vehicles must be fitted with converters to remove various pollutants produced by diesel engines. Diesel produces less nitrogen oxides, carbon monoxide and carbon dioxide, but more soot. The technology to scrub diesel exhaust fumes is being developed, although the European Community lags behind the USA in insisting on their mandatory use.

It should not be forgotten that there are numerous models of petrol driven cars that also achieve high rates of fuel efficiency.

Unfortunately, since the fall in oil prices interest in increasing fuel economy has declined and better engine design has often been translated into higher powered cars rather than ones with higher fuel efficiencies. The complacent attitudes of governments towards oil conservation is extremely myopic even in the narrow terms of their own objectives. Oil consumption is once more rising fast, a major cause of which is rising consumption by motor vehicles. The world is now consuming almost as much oil as it did in 1979, the peak year of global oil consumption. If present trends continue, by the mid 1990s OPEC states will be producing oil in excess of 90 per cent of their capacity, the level that saw turmoil in Iran spark off the last oil crisis. Another oil crisis would be a savage way of encouraging energy efficiency! One would have thought that inducing faster progress in motor vehicle fuel economy technology would be a major priority for geopolitical, never mind environmental, reasons.

Doubling motor vehicle fuel efficiency within a decade would require that stringent minimum fuel efficiency standards were set and vehicle taxation was oriented towards rewarding fuel efficiency.

Company car tax perks should be removed. The steady drift towards company car ownership in the UK (encouraged by the 'income in kind' company car) has probably retarded improvement in fuel efficiency. The UK's average car fuel efficiency lags behind other European countries as shown in Table 3.2.

Table 3.2: Motor spirit consumption per car in 1971 and 1985 (tonnes p.a.)

Country	1971	1985	% change
United Kingdom	1.16	1.08	−7
France	0.93	0.70	−25
Belgium	1.01	0.76	−25
W. Germany	1.02	0.98	−4
Denmark	1.31	1.05	−19
Italy	0.92	0.54	−40
Netherlands	1.08	1.11	+2
Ireland	1.50	1.24	−17
USA	2.68	2.26	−15

Source: Submission by Open University Energy and Environment Research Unit to the Select Committee on Energy's Enquiry into the Greenhouse Effect. February 1989, p. 41.

The benefits from company cars should be taxed at their real value. Company cars should be fitted with speed governors to stop them exceeding 75 mph. The government could order this change under existing health and safety at work law which legitimises action to stop employees using machinery in such a way as to break the law. Speed governors will have a payback of around 12 weeks because of the resulting fuel savings. Speed governors could later be fitted to all cars.

Tax incentives like zero road tax should be given to fuel efficient cars, such as those achieving 100 miles per gallon at 56 mph. The road tax on inefficient cars could be increased. Alternatively, road tax could simply be abolished and the revenue gained instead from increased fuel taxation.

Speed limits should be reduced both as a safety measure, and as a measure that will improve fuel efficiency.

Although such policies must be implemented with maximum speed and determination, they will, on their own, be insufficient to reduce carbon dioxide emissions if car use increases at the same, or perhaps an even greater rate than improvements in fuel efficiency.

The global situation is very gloomy, with car ownership increasing at something approaching an exponential rate. There were under 50 million cars across the planet in 1950. In 1980 there were 210 million. It is likely that by the year 2000 the number of cars will be moving towards the 500 million mark.

If there was the same people-to-car ratio in the whole of the world as in the USA there would be over 3000 million cars in the world by the year 2000, a truly frightening prospect as far as global warming is concerned. It seems unlikely that fuel efficiency technology could keep sufficient pace with such growth in numbers to stop a large absolute increase in carbon dioxide emissions from motor vehicles.

Of course, low incomes in less developed countries will mean that a three or four thousand million car world will not be reached for many years. Supporters of the motor car may hope that by then solar cars, cars run on batteries replenished by renewable energy sources, or cars run on hydrogen electrolysed by renewable electricity, may avert car-induced environmental catastrophe!

Clearly some cars will be needed in the future, and provided the exponential increase in car use can be arrested, motor transport can be sustainable if cars are powered by renewable sources. Technology involving lead batteries seems limited by the fact that the world would run out of lead. The most attractive fuel

Figure 3.3

option for the long term could be hydrogen. Hydrogen could be produced by using electricity from renewable sources to hydrolyse water. The hydrogen could then be used in fuel cells to produce electricity which would power the motor vehicle. This would be a good way of making full use of intermittent renewable energy sources.

Although the theory seems fine, the technology is far from perfected. This type of strategy should command a great deal more research attention than is currently being given. Nevertheless, as attractive as such a strategy may be in the long term, we have to develop policies to deal with the explosion in motor car use that is occurring now.

Also, the adoption of renewable technologies by the motor industry will do nothing to stop the destruction caused by road building and other effects of increased car numbers. On top of this, the production of thousands of millions of cars will in itself consume vast quantities of energy.

Many of the world's major cities are already grinding to a halt and several of them – such as Athens, Milan and Los Angeles – are deploying restraints on car use. In California the smog problem has driven the state to adopt several drastic measures, including the imposition of limits on the number of cars per family. Car pooling schemes have been promoted; some roads have been reserved for cars carrying more than one person. This has also been tried out in Japan. It has led to some bizarre attempts to evade the regulations. One Japanese driver was found to have had her dead husband propped up in the passenger seat for weeks!

In California driving on petrol and diesel will be illegal after 2007. Petroleum will be replaced, most probably, by ethanol and methanol fuels. But what impact is this likely to have on global warming?

The alcohol-as-fuel strategy may ease smog problems and reduce some greenhouse inducing emissions (although some evidence suggests that the gains in these respects may be only partial), but it is unlikely to significantly reduce carbon dioxide emissions from motor vehicles since the methanol would be mostly produced from fossil fuels.

Ethanol based fuels would come from energy crops grown by farmers. Energy crops absorb carbon dioxide when they are growing and will give off no more carbon dioxide when they are burned than they absorbed during growth. Thus energy crops do not add to global warming, provided of course that they are replanted. Currently such fuels are rather expensive, although the prices could be kept down by subsidies or made relatively cheaper by increasing the prices of fossil fuels through differential energy taxation.

Unfortunately there just is not enough farmland available to produce more than a small proportion of total UK fuel demand. A third of Britain would have to go over to crop production to meet just 10 per cent of UK demand for car fuels.[14] Growing trees to provide electricity or heat is a much better use of resources. Energy forestry achieves higher productivity than growing plants for alcohol since trees store many times more carbon per hectare than other forms of vegetation. In addition

energy forestry avoids the problems created by growing monoc-
ultures because it involves using a variety of strains of tree. I
shall comment more about this in Chapter Four.

The use of alcohol based fuels is not likely to be more than a
partial answer to car-induced global warming problems,
although the Californian ban on petrol driven cars is to be
welcomed since it will speed up development of other types of
fuel. It seems that one effect of this ban will be to favour cars
run on electricity. Electric cars will indeed cut smog problems,
but if the electricity comes originally from fossil fuelled power
stations the end product could be even more global warming,
particularly if there is little use of combined heat and power.

At the moment the biggest lesson we can learn from America
is that social atomisation, congestion, and air pollution in many
US cities act as a sad testament to a society based on unrestrained
market forces and a lack of urban and transport planning. Developing nations appear to be repeating the mistakes made by the
industrialised world.

The adoption of catalytic converter technology, which reduces
emissions of nitrogen oxides (causing acid rain), carbon monoxide (causing heart disease and, indirectly, global warming because
it reduces the ability of the atmosphere to absorb methane which
is a very powerful greenhouse gas) and hydrocarbons (causing
ozone and photochemical smog when combined with sunlight
and other car pollutants), has reduced some of the pollution
caused by cars in the USA.

However, even though catalytic converters theoretically
remove up to 90 per cent of such pollutants, in reality the
difficulties of monitoring the performance of ageing cars and
ageing converters means the pollution reduction is much smaller.
Despite years of cars being fitted with converters, Los Angeles'
smog problems are as bad as ever.

There are many areas of economic activity in which it can be
said that sustainability can be reconciled with growth. But the
continued unrestricted growth of petrol, or for that matter alcohol, powered motor cars does not seem, on the basis of currently
available evidence, to be reconcilable with ecological sustainability.

A variety of tactics need to be applied to restrict car use in urban areas. 'Road calming' involving narrower streets and ramps to slow cars and help cyclists, cycle lanes, and road pricing schemes all need to be adopted in the context of heavy investment in, and subsidy of, public transport.

Because of the convenience and psychological attractiveness of cars, road pricing in urban areas may have to be set at very high levels in order to be effective. This may have deleterious effects on some businesses. However, part of the problem in which we are now deeply enmeshed is that society has been designed to fit the requirements of the motor car. This should be reversed and we should plan towns and cities in such a way that dependence on the motor car is reduced. By doing this the economic costs of reducing reliance on motor vehicles will be cut.

The environmental and social consequences of policies that otherwise appear cost-effective in balance sheet terms need to be taken into account when deciding social, planning and taxation policy. Motorists may complain bitterly about increased taxation on road use, but if the full environmental and social costs of motor cars were charged to motorists then they would, at least in urban areas where fuel economy is at its lowest and traffic congestion at its worst, be priced off the road.

The policies I have described will run into heavy opposition, particularly from powerful vested interests such as companies that build roads. A population which is used to running cars will need good reasons to accept policies which shift resources away from motor cars. However, such policies can be clearly justified. Public opinion is likely to recognise this before governments. In both local and global terms the situation is desperate. We must act now.

INDUSTRY

The programme of the UK Energy Efficiency Office (EEO) has been most noticeable in the industrial sector where its claim to have saved several hundreds of millions of pounds a year in energy bills is probably justified. It has promoted energy efficient processes that have been worked out by the Energy Technology Support Unit (ESTU) based at Harwell.

The EEO has been working through companies, starting off with the largest, at a fairly slow pace. The Department of Energy feels that once industry has got the message about energy efficiency, the market will do the rest.

The EEO's industrial programme is inadequate. First because it is dealing with companies on a 'one off' basis. There is no clear mechanism of keeping up with new ways of saving energy. Second, mere provision of information about energy efficiency does not overcome the psychological and economic obstacles to energy conservation.

Firms may not be interested in energy saving measures if they have a long payback period. If there is a choice between, on the one hand, putting in new production plant and, on the other hand, installing energy saving equipment, each of which will give approximately the same returns, the tangible new production plant will invariably be chosen over the intangible possibility of future energy savings. Many firms may not be very interested in energy conservation because energy makes up only a small part of their costs.

Furthermore the institutional structure of the average company, which is organised towards making money out of production rather than saving, puts conservation at a disadvantage when investment decisions are made, even when there is a clear case for spending on energy saving.

This situation can only be overcome by a combination of larger research programmes by ETSU, regulation, tax incentives, high carbon taxes and greater political enthusiasm for conservation from both workers and managers.

Tax incentive schemes are used in places like West Germany, which has given a tax allowance for investment in energy conservation equipment, including, for example, combined heat and power plant. In the UK the Select Committee on Energy's enquiry into the implications of the greenhouse effect backed the idea of tax incentives for conservation saying:

For example, allowing only, say, 90 per cent of a firm's energy costs to be allowable against tax while a tax allowance of, perhaps, 110 per cent is given for investment in energy efficiency equipment might encourage firms to look more closely at their energy bills.[15]

Another idea might be to set up an energy efficiency inspectorate. Companies over a certain size could be given a statutory responsibility to draw up regular energy audits, and these could be assessed by the inspectorate. This in itself would encourage firms to appoint more energy managers and to give them higher status.

Energy inspectors could have the power to prosecute firms that were not fulfilling their energy management responsibilities. The inspectors should recommend specific energy saving strategies where appropriate. If these were not implemented, the inspectors should have the power to insert a statement in the annual shareholders' report describing the missed energy conservation opportunities.

Government departments and local authorities should increase and upgrade the number of energy managers they employ.

There is a pressing case for greens to be active in trade unions in order to campaign for energy efficiency gains in both the production of the goods and the amount of energy that the goods themselves consume after they have been sold.

We must achieve greater regulation of the market in order to achieve energy efficiency gains, but such a strategy cannot rely on national policy alone. People working at the grass roots in collaboration with trained personnel must be an essential part of the formula.

HOW MUCH ENERGY CONSERVATION?

The level of achievable energy conservation depends to a large extent on the strength of political will to push for conservation measures and methods. Very large reductions are possible.

In 1979 Gerald Leach and others published *A Low Energy Strategy for the UK*[16] which suggested that conservation policies could reduce energy consumption. This, for its day, was an astounding claim.

Yet Leach's work, which projected that energy consumption

in 2025 would be 8 per cent less than in 1976 on the basis of a 2.2 per cent per annum rate of economic growth, now looks conservative. UK energy consumption in 1987 was already less than in 1976, though due mainly to a shift from manufacturing to service industries.

The recent improvement in building regulations makes them tighter than those Leach assumed for the whole of the period to 2025 (although they are still a long way behind standards in Canada and Scandinavia). Power stations have already become much more efficient than he anticipated, with even more efficient gas combined cycle and advanced coal stations still to be put on line. Furthermore Leach's assumed levels of efficiency improvement of car engines and electrical appliances were conservative. If the full range of conservationist policies were applied the savings could be much larger than the levels anticipated by Leach.

In 1983 Olivier and others produced *Energy Efficient Futures*,[11] a very detailed study saying that the UK's primary energy consumption could be reduced by between a third and almost half of its present levels by 2025 (depending on the rate of technical change) while gross domestic product increased by 2.9 times its 1976 level. Olivier and his colleagues assumed established rates of replacement for appliances, motors, production systems, houses and vehicles. They also assumed that energy prices were not kept artificially low by subsidies, and that policies such as those I have mentioned were vigorously implemented and conservationist practices given high governmental and consumer priority.

By 2025 all dwellings have central heating at 21°C, every household has a fridge, freezer, washing machine, clothes drier, dishwasher and colour TV. The number of households with cars increases from 56 per cent in 1976 to 75 per cent in 2025 (although the number of car owning households had already leapt to 70 per cent by 1985).

The study also included two 'conserver' scenarios in which people gave materialism a much lower priority and production of material goods reached a plateau, after the year 2000. In these scenarios energy consumption was reduced by up to 70 per cent.

However, although the study did propose political instruments that would improve energy efficiency it did not suggest any political instruments that would force people to give materialism a much lower priority.

The UK should set a target of reducing its energy demand by 1.8 per cent per year. If continued over a 35 year period this would reduce energy consumption by around 47 per cent. Such a target should be accompanied by vigorous steps to implement a conservation programme similar to that which I have already outlined, through use of regulatory and fiscal measures and institutional changes.

If these steps were accompanied by energetic deployment of renewable energy sources, and some switching from high carbon coal and oil to lower carbon gas, we should reduce the UK's carbon dioxide output by over 20 per cent by 2005, while at the same time phasing out nuclear power. If this strategy was continued, we could reduce carbon dioxide emissions by 60 per cent by the year 2025.

I shall give greater consideration to future energy scenarios after I have looked at the supply side of energy policy. Energy conservation is of central importance to any sustainable energy strategy, but we still need energy from somewhere.

4 Supplying Energy

COAL

In recent years efficient fluidised bed combustion power stations have been developed which can be used in CHP/district heating systems to cut down on the production of carbon dioxide and eliminate the large bulk of sulphur and nitrogen oxide emissions that cause acid rain.

Around three-quarters of UK coal consumption is through electricity production, so such developments will make UK coal use more environmentally acceptable, and clearly there remains an important role for coal in energy provision.

But much less coal will be used if conservation strategies are successful. Less coal will be needed to produce a given amount of energy and less energy should be demanded overall. Crucially, we need to aim to burn less coal as part of a strategy of combatting global warming.

Increased use of renewables will displace fossil fuels in general. On top of this many argue that there should be at least some substitution of high carbon coal by lower carbon gas.

Whatever the relative importance of these various tactics may be, a sustainable energy strategy demands that coal consumption needs to be steadily reduced. The only way to avoid this conclusion is to argue that the greenhouse effect should not be taken seriously, a position I would strongly reject.

Other arguments sometimes deployed suggest that coal or coal fired power stations contribute so little to the greenhouse effect that we really do not need to cut coal consumption. Such logic is erroneous on several grounds.

The claim made for instance by K. M. Sullivan of the International Coal Development Institute[1] that coal fired power stations contribute only 6 per cent of the greenhouse effect is true on paper, but very misleading. For a start this is a percentage of the total contribution from greenhouse gases, not just the half from carbon dioxide. In fact coal from all sources contributes over 43 per cent of UK energy-related carbon dioxide emissions. It is by far the largest single source of carbon dioxide.

The 6 per cent claim is also misleading because as the developing nations industrialise, so this figure increases. In the UK, for example, coal fired power stations make up at least 13 per cent of this country's contribution to increasing the greenhouse effect. How on earth can we persuade the Chinese not to accelerate consumption of their immense coal reserves if we do not cut down on our own coal consumption?

We can divide up the various sources of global warming into numerous apparently 'small' packages: carbon dioxide from cars, industry, the home; CFCs from refrigerators, aerosols, packaging; methane from cows, rice paddies; nitrous oxide from fertilisers, etc. No doubt all the interest groups connected with these activities can argue their corner saying that their contribution is only small, so why worry about it? If we are going to do anything about the greenhouse effect, we must reduce as many sources as possible by as much as is practicable.

The anti-nuclear movement has for obvious political reasons backed increased coal use as a method of phasing out nuclear power. After all, the UK has large coal reserves. However, the left must acclimatise itself to seeking other ways of phasing out nuclear power.

The United Nations Environment Programme is hoping to achieve a global pact restricting carbon dioxide emissions in the next couple of years. We cannot stand in the way.

We should ensure that all present coal fired stations are fitted with flue gas desulphurising equipment and that such new coal power stations that are built are pressurised fluidised bed combustors which greatly reduce acid rain producing emissions of sulphur dioxide and nitrogen oxides. These stations should preferably be small, fitted with CHP and connected to district heating systems.

Unfortunately such scrubbing techniques cannot be practicably applied to carbon dioxide. There are organic solvents that could absorb the carbon dioxide and vast arrays of pipelines could be built to take the gas to the sea bed. Such a programme would be incredibly expensive, would present great potential environmental hazards, and there is no guarantee that the carbon dioxide would not eventually seep through to the atmosphere.

The above argument impels us to reduce coal burning, but this should not be confused with the policies advocated by the present government which pursues class politics cloaked in ecology.

For example, sapping the UK coal industry by allowing the privatised electricity companies to increase the levels of coal imports from sources like South Africa will do nothing to stop global warming. Indeed, if plans to build ports to receive coal imports continue, we could in the future face the situation where coal demand has not only been decreased by energy conservation and perhaps fuel switching strategies, but also by the possibility that much of the remaining balance will be produced overseas.

The government's reluctance to finance further research into more efficient, cleaner types of coal fired power stations cannot be justified on environmental grounds. The demands made by the National Union of Mineworkers for greater development and adoption of advanced coal burning technology and for more action to tackle acid rain should be fully supported. New types of pressurised fluidised bed boilers promise to increase the efficiency of coal fired stations towards the 50 per cent mark. The most efficient coal stations currently in operation have efficiencies of around 38 per cent.

Fluidised bed combustion involves burning coal that has been crushed into fine particles. It is not only more efficient but it also allows the coal to be mixed with limestone so that most of the sulphur (which leads to acid rain promoting sulphur dioxide) can be removed. Because the coal is burnt at a lower temperature than in conventional stations, only small quantities of nitrogen oxides (which also produce acid rain) are produced.

Although it is certainly the case that coal, burnt in more efficient stations associated with CHP systems, will contribute a large proportion of our energy requirements for a long time to come our political sympathy with the miners should not blind us to the need to reduce coal consumption. This is not good news to the miners. But rather than trying to defend the current unsustainable levels of coal burning the left should instead spend time investigating employment alternatives. This should primarily involve support and encouragement for threatened communities in drawing up their own plans for alternative employment.

OIL

Political, quite apart from ecological considerations have pushed the demand for oil conservation to the top of the energy policy agenda, although interest in conservation declined in the aftermath of the two oil crises.

Conservation of oil, particularly in the transport sector where almost half of the UK's total oil is consumed, has not been a policy priority in recent years. Neither has there been any real effort to ensure that the proceeds of North Sea oil are channeled into domestic investment. Rather the oil money has been frittered away by the Conservatives to support, for example, the pre-1987 election Lawson boom. This boom would not have been sustainable but for North Sea oil's positive contribution to our balance of payments.

The government has rejected any accommodation with OPEC that might obtain oil price stability on the world market. High oil prices may have encouraged better energy efficiency, but it has also encouraged substitution by coal and put pressure on developing nations short of foreign exchange. The environment has suffered as developing nations try to generate more cash crops to pay for oil imports.

Rather than respond to the Brandt Report's call for stable oil prices and expanded aid programmes the western based International Energy Agency has advocated nuclear power expansion.

One would have thought that the most practical, immediate tactic would be to adopt common standards of fuel efficiency in motor vehicles, and to pursue practical policies that will reduce

the demand for cars. Oil could be replaced by gas in power
stations and a range of industrial and heating uses.

Many oil analysts, with the important exception of Peter
Odell, believe that a further oil crisis is inevitable as world oil
consumption again rises towards its 1979 peak. Declining US
oil production and increasing US reliance on imported oil will
exacerbate the situation. Vigorous, internationally agreed policies of energy conservation are required not only to stave off
damaging oil crises but also to ameliorate the more permanent
threat of global warming.

Besides reducing oil consumption by the already mentioned
conservation strategies, we should ensure that oil is replaced by
natural gas in as many uses as possible. Since the oil crises the
amount of electricity generated from oil has greatly declined.
Oil should be replaced by gas in electricity generation. Gas could
also be used as a substitute for petrol in cars.

GAS

Natural gas has many attractions to those like Krause and Goldemberg who seek to combat global warming. Gas produces
much less carbon dioxide than coal and oil. In addition gas can
be 'cleaned' much more easily and comprehensively than coal to
remove pollutants that produce acid rain.

On the other hand gas can have considerable environmental
impacts mostly resulting from its explosive potential, although
these can be set against oil spillages and the various hazards of
coal mining. Natural gas seepages from pipelines and production
will also produce global warming. However, according to Mike
Grubb who has produced an analysis of the impact of gas seepages from various sources, gas still has a big advantage over coal
in terms of their relative contributions to global warming. He
comments that 'the radiative benefits of coal to gas switching
are more like 2/3 than the commonly cited 1/2 in many cases,
depending somewhat on local circumstances.'[2]

Gas escapes from power stations are likely to be much less
than from systems delivering gas to domestic consumers. Nevertheless, it is important that regulations be enacted requiring that

seepages be kept down to a prescribed minimum. Such a law already exists in the USA.

The new generation of gas power plants, combined cycle turbines, are very efficient, cheap and quick to build, and have efficiencies of around 50 per cent, which compares to the average efficiency of UK power stations of around 38 per cent. Combined cycle turbines contribute to the development of a more flexible electricity supply industry since they can be started up more quickly than conventional steam generators.

Now that a European Community ruling has forced British Gas to curb its monopoly practices and allow gas power stations direct access to gas fields there is increasing interest in not only gas turbines but also gas powered industrial combined heat and power systems.

Until fairly recently most experts agreed that gas reserves were relatively small, thus limiting natural gas as a fuel of the future. However current estimates of gas reserves are far more optimistic with British North Sea gas fields and even Holland's Groningen field lasting much longer than was anticipated. Norway has discovered the giant Troll field.

Many energy analysts believe that gas reserves are far larger than reserves of oil. Hans Holger-Rogner, for example, writing in *Energy Policy*[3] argues that we are seeing a new cycle of fuel substitution, with gas becoming the dominant fossil fuel in the future. Such an outlook may yet prove an exaggeration. We can still not be sure that gas reserves are as plentiful as some suggest. Nevertheless, provided that we pursue an overall energy policy that is oriented towards conservation, a policy of substituting gas for coal and oil has too many environmental and economic attractions to be easily brushed aside, or even to be resisted.

We could certainly reduce the UK's carbon output to some extent by shifting the mix of fossil fuel used in electricity production more towards gas. Gas plants must be geared towards CHP. Conservation policies should reduce demand for gas overall as, for instance, gas heating is replaced by district heating and energy efficiency policies in general take effect.

However much we conserve energy, or even follow what is

only a partial and transitional strategy of replacing coal and oil by gas, we still need to replace fossil by non-fossil fuel sources.

THE NEED FOR RENEWABLE ENERGY SOURCES

The pressing need to deploy renewable sources of energy is demonstrated by an inspection of high energy efficiency scenarios such as that put forward by Goldemberg and others in their *Energy for a Sustainable World*, published by the World Resources Institute (see Figure 4.1).

This scenario sees energy demand falling in the industrialised world, although it increases in developing countries. It says that if the improvements that they recommend are fully implemented,

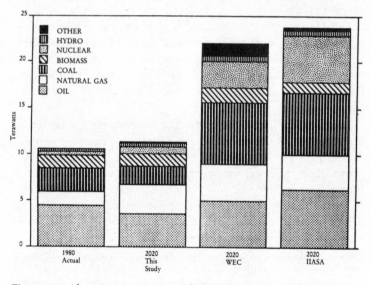

Figure 4.1: Alternative projections of global energy use. This study: WRI scenario; WEC: World Energy Conference; IIASA: International Institute for Applied Systems Analysis. The latter two projections are the averages of the high and low scenarios developed by the respective groups. [Source: Goldemberg, J. and others, Energy for a Sustainable World, *World Resources Institute, Washington DC, 1987. Cited by J. Koras and M. Kelly,* The Heat Trap, *Friends of the Earth, London, 1989, page 18.]*

then by 2020 global energy demand will have increased by less than 10 per cent. This scenario is much lower than conventional scenarios which predict energy demand to rise to well over twice its present level by 2020.

In the industrialised world per capita energy consumption is cut by half. In the developing world per capita consumption increases by 30 per cent, although they are still far behind the industrialised nations in both energy consumption and living standards.

Even in the Goldemberg 'energy efficiency' scenario, fossil fuel derived carbon dioxide emissions would fall by only between 5 and 10 per cent, and this gain is partly attributable to a significant switching from coal and oil to gas. The Goldemberg scenario includes only very marginal increases in energy derived from renewable sources.

Given the likely pressure for higher standards of living in the developing world, and the fact that the United Nations projects world population to double before stabilising sometime after 2050, the sort of reductions in carbon dioxide emissions demanded by the Toronto Conference are unlikely to be achieved without increasing the level of non-fossil energy sources.

If we are to avoid use of nuclear power with all its environmental, political and economic disadvantages, the only alternative is the speedy deployment of renewable energy sources.

Ecologists have preferred renewables on the basis that they are 'clean' sources of energy that do not deplete natural resources and that keep pollution to a minimum. But this does not mean they are without environmental impact. In fact sometimes they have generated as much opposition as nuclear power, as can be seen in the emotions produced by proposals to build hydroelectric dams. Large scale hydropower requires extensive areas to be flooded and the destruction of entire communities and large swathes of wildlife habitats. In Sweden both the nuclear power and the hydroelectricity expansion programmes have been halted on environmental grounds. Sweden hopes to phase out nuclear power.

In recent times fears have been raised about the environmental impact of sources like tidal energy and wind power. There are also environmental consequences of one sort or another from energy sources such as wood energy crops, refuse derived fuel, geothermal energy and even solar power.

The truth of the matter is that there is no energy source that is completely without environmental impact. However we must realise that although energy conservation is vitally important, it is not enough on its own.

We still need to replace fossil fuel sources with energy from alternative sources. This is bound to produce environmental problems, although to be justified the alternative energy sources must create less environmental disruption than the fossil fuel sources they replace.

The only ultimately pure green solution that would remove human environmental impact completely would be for humanity to commit collective suicide. Yet this is precisely the scenario that we wish to avoid.

In an imperfect world we must make choices, and the only way we can do this rationally is to decide priorities. Of course even such rationalism involves making value judgements, but unless we at least attempt to structure the argument around well-defined priorities, we can hardly claim to be basing our decisions on the concept of sustainability. What should these priorities be?

ENVIRONMENTAL PRIORITIES

I began this book by stating that the overriding priority governing our choice of energy policies should be that they are sustainable in global terms. This must include reducing the burning of fossil fuels.

But non-fossil energy sources which add little to global warming will have their own, usually local, environmental effects. Nuclear power has several types of environmental impact and has real or potential disadvantageous social and political effects.

Often there is conflict between global and local priorities. In the case of wind power, for example, there is a trade-off between what some may see as a local visual intrusion and the impact of

Figure 4.2: Energy sources without environmental impact. I think this is a complete list . . .

the carbon dioxide emissions that would be produced by a fossil fuel source that the wind generation is supposed to replace.

Given the obvious fact that energy has to come from somewhere, we need some way of measuring the different impacts of various energy sources.

We can only solve this environmental dilemma by doing a comparative environmental impact assessment. This involves assessing the external costs of different energy options. Such external costs consist mainly of environmental factors, including damage to flora and fauna, fossil fuel and uranium depletion, the risks to human health, the damage to buildings and materials (caused for example by acid rain), the damage caused by rises in sea level and various other consequences of global warming, the risks of accidents, the loss of amenities, visual intrusion and so on.

In practice such costs are very difficult to work out. There is a growing body of work on monetary valuation of environmental costs and benefits of different types of development, including some on energy sources. Such analysis can be useful in translating local environmental impact into cost terms, but it is going to be very difficult to estimate, for example, the 'global warming cost' of a fossil fuel power station.

There is a very large degree of uncertainty about the amount of global warming that will be caused by a given amount of fossil fuel burning and perhaps even greater uncertainty about the likely climatic, never mind social and zoological changes that result from such global warming.

Nevertheless the work that has been done on monetarising the environmental impact of renewable versus conventional energy sources suggests that renewables win hands down.

In a study commissioned by the California Energy Commission, Mike De Angelis and Sam Rushkin concluded that wind and biomass sources are the most cost-effective forms of electricity generation when the external costs of energy production are taken into account.

Olav Hohmeyer, in his European Commission-sponsored study *The Social Costs of Energy Consumption*, found that when the social costs of nuclear and fossil fuel produced electricity were taken into account, wind power was already the cheapest option for electricity generation in West Germany. Since the social costs of nuclear and fossil fuel electricity are rising and the costs of wind power are falling, wind's advantage is likely to grow as we go farther into the future.

Having assessed the external costs, Hohmeyer calculates that 'internalising' the social costs of conventional electricity supplies would increase electricity prices in West Germany by around 50 to 110 per cent. Hohmeyer concludes that after the external social costs of electricity from coal and nuclear power are taken into account even solar photovoltaics will, by the year 2005, be cheaper than conventionally produced electricity, provided that the costs of solar electricity continue to decline at recent rates. He comments:

> Compared to the use of conventional non-renewable energy sources, the use of renewable energy sources produces very few or no external costs and may even cause positive external effects. This discrepancy, which is not reflected in the relative energy prices, causes a serious distortion of the energy markets. As substantial costs to society are not considered in the allocation process, wrong decisions are produced by the market mechanism.[4]

Hohmeyer recommends that the market distortion be removed by giving subsidies to renewables and financing such subsidies out of energy taxation. In fact Hohmeyer's study almost certainly *understates* the advantage of wind power over nuclear and fossil fuel electricity because he makes only a small allowance for the social costs of climatic change compared to, for example, acid rain. He includes only the costs of upgrading German coastal sea defences to deal with expected sea level rises over the next fifty years. Yet in the case of the UK, which has much more coastline and vulnerable low-lying land, such costs are likely to be much higher. Rather more importantly, no attempt is made to 'internalise' the costs to other nations of West German fossil fuel emissions. Such costs could – in the case of for instance Bangladesh – be equivalent to a major portion of the gross domestic product. The costs of protecting the low-lying Maldive Islands against sea level rises would be infinitely high. There are a number of other consequences of climatic change, to which I have already referred, that should really also be taken into account.

Of course there are some circumstances where renewables do have very major social costs. Large hydroelectric power schemes are a case in point. Although we may conclude that the devastating impact of large hydroelectric projects rules them out as ways of fighting global warming, what is our approach when for example we examine the case of tidal power stations? Tidal power projects will disturb some local wild life, although many times less than large hydro schemes.

However, assessing such impacts must not be the only factors in the equation. If we are already maximising energy efficiency the environmental cost of not deploying the tidal scheme will include global warming if, instead, the electricity is generated from fossil fuels.

Given that many naturalists are very worried that many bird species and other types of wildlife will be unable to adapt to sudden climatic changes caused by global warming, a decision not to deploy tidal power could, on balance, act to destroy much more wildlife than would be protected by such a decision. It would certainly do a lot of damage to many humans.

In these situations we must decide whether the environmental consequences of a particular renewable source are greater or less than the environmental consequences of a nuclear or fossil fuel source that would provide the same amount of electricity.

Monetary evaluations of environmental effects of energy sources are useful devices to help us compare different energy options. But such tools are still, in many senses, primitive devices and are often subject to widely differing interpretation.

In the end we shall have to rely on political judgement. Such judgement should be conditioned by the realisation that even with maximum energy efficiency we still need non-fossil power supplies and that if such power supplies do not come from renewables they may well come from nuclear power. Faced with this range of choices, even an increasingly 'greened' population is unlikely to choose the only other option, that of unplugging their electrical appliances.

I believe that the relatively minor environmental impacts of renewable sources such as wind, tidal, geothermal and wave power, energy forestry and biomass waste sources are almost certain to be outweighed by the impact of global warming produced by equivalently rated fossil fuel power stations.

I shall now look at the practicalities of bringing renewable sources on line. But first, what is the current use of, and interest in, renewable energy sources?

INTEREST IN RENEWABLE SOURCES OF ENERGY

Up to a fifth of world energy supplies already comes from renewable energy sources: up to 14 per cent from biomass, and 6 per cent from hydroelectric power.

In California, where tax incentives and political tastes favour renewables, renewable sources (as well as low carbon producing gas cogeneration) now have a capacity of more than half the UK's nuclear generating capacity. Wind power generation expanded to 1.5GW of capacity after only 4 years. Biofuels, and, increasingly, geothermal energy sources also produce significant proportions of California's energy requirements.

The Danes and the Dutch plan to provide 10 per cent of their electricity from wind turbines by the year 2000. The Dutch have given 40 per cent capital grants as incentives to wind turbine companies. The UK's wind energy resources are many times greater than those of Denmark or Holland. Sweden derives over an eighth of its total energy requirements from biomass sources alone, Nicaragua produces 25 per cent of its electricity from geothermal energy, the French have a tidal power scheme at La Rance, and so on.

Yet the UK lags behind, spending less money on a per capita basis on renewable research than a relatively poor country like Greece. Compared to most other developed nations, this country's level of private interest in renewables is embarrassingly small.

TABLE 4.1: Government research and development spending on renewables in selected countries, 1986

Country	Renewables R&D spending (Million dollars)	Share of energy R&D budget (per cent)	Spending per capita (dollars)
Sweden	17.3	21.8	2.06
Switzerland	10.2	14.7	1.57
Netherlands	17.0	10.6	1.17
West Germany	65.9	11.6	1.09
Greece	9.7	63.2	0.97
Japan	99.2	4.3	0.82
United States	177.2	7.8	0.73
Italy	29.5	3.9	0.52
Denmark	2.6	17.8	0.51
Spain	19.4	27.6	0.50
United Kingdom	16.6	4.4	0.29

Source: Network for Alternative Technology and Technology Assessment (NATTA) Newsletter 53, May/June 1988, p. 23.

RENEWABLES IN THE UK

Although the UK uses significant amounts of hydroelectricity, renewable energy sources like wind, wave, geothermal, tidal, biofuels and solar, have always been treated as poor relations compared to nuclear power. In recent years the funding of UK research into nuclear power has been around £200 million per year, while renewables have been given about £15 million.

The Department of Energy has no plans to right this imbalance, but instead plans for a long term decrease in government-funded renewable research in the expectation that private sector investment in renewables will take off.

Yet no post-war UK government has ever had this sort of 'leave it to the market' attitude to research and development of nuclear power. The reasons for this disparity are political and ideological rather than technical.

Nuclear fission programmes would never have started but for the nuclear weapons programme and a social ideology which seeks human and industrial domination of nature rather than harmony with the ecosphere.

The Department of Energy has said that up to around 70TWh of electricity and up to 20 MTCE of heat could come each year from renewable sources by 2025, compared to 1987 UK electricity consumption of 250TWh and total UK primary energy consumption of 330MTCE.[5]

I shall demonstrate that at least the Department of Energy's figure for potential renewable electricity is an underestimate. Between 90TWh and 140TWh of renewable electricity could be produced by 2025, to provide upwards of 60 per cent of a reduced total electricity demand. If we assume that electricity demand can be cut by at least a third, as discussed earlier in the book, then by 2025 it is possible that two thirds of electricity could be supplied from renewable electricity sources alone. The remaining third could be provided by small scale gas and coal CHP power stations linked to district heating networks.

In the energy economy as a whole, by 2025 a quarter of UK primary energy requirements could come from renewable energy sources. These estimates are based on currently practicable technology and economic competitiveness, or in some cases, that which is widely agreed will be economically competitive in the near future. An energetic research and development effort would almost certainly increase the range of practicably deployable renewable technologies by 2025. My estimates are conservative in that they do not take account of such developments. These claims are also based on the general assumption that conservation policies achieve a reduction in UK primary energy consumption of 32 to 47 per cent by the year 2025.

Provided that there is a major stepping-up of research and development into renewables (in most cases this means development rather than fundamental research), and refinements of existing technologies, we could have 50 per cent of UK primary energy produced from renewables by or soon after 2050.

However, I am concerned to sketch in at least the outlines of a practical strategy for deployment of renewable sources in the short and medium term. Although some renewable technologies such as offshore wind, wave power, photovoltaics and hot dry rock geothermal energy require to a greater or lesser extent further research, others like onshore wind, tidal power, passive solar power and various types of biomass can be deployed now. Even offshore wind is being deployed by other nations, although not by this country which has among the best offshore resources in the world.

I shall look at the practicalities of energy from, in order, wind, biomass, tidal, hydroelectric, wave, geothermal and solar sources and then consider some of the policies that might encourage the deployment of renewable energy sources.

WIND POWER

Evidence from the Central Electricity Generating Board (CEGB) to a 1988 House of Lords Select Committee hearing on alternative energy sources indicated that up to 17 per cent of the UK's electricity supply could come from onshore wind turbines and that offshore wind resources sited in shallow waters off East Anglia were comparable to the UK's total electricity requirements.

The evidence reported that onshore wind power was competitive in price terms. Indeed the best potential wind sites would seem to offer electricity supplies at prices rather better than coal or oil, and certainly nuclear power.

Nevertheless the establishment's attitude to wind power has been reluctant compared to dominant attitudes in Denmark and Holland. The CEGB is still completing its plans for its first inland wind farms, and is cautious about the plans for the future, projecting that there will be no more than 1GW of wind generators installed by the year 2000. Many supporters of wind power have felt that the CEGB's proposals for wind farms have been deliberately insensitive, at least in one case, in Durham, where it was proposed to build a farm in an area of outstanding natural beauty.

Certainly the enthusiasm in non-nuclear Denmark for wind is in marked contrast to the UK where the electricity supply industry is festooned with former employees of the Atomic Energy Authority.

British Nuclear Fuels has conducted a massive campaign of disinformation about alternative energy strategies, implying in at least one advertisement that significant deployment of onshore wind power would cover large areas of the country.[6] Although it is certainly the case that wind farms take up large amounts of space, not even a single building would be threatened by large-scale windpower deployment.

An exhaustive study of the environmental effect of wind power was compiled by Alexei Clarke[7] who concluded that although some environmental impact and some public disquiet was inevitable there was enough land well away from dwellings, villages or environmentally sensitive locations to allow 10 to 20 per cent of the UK's present level of electricity supply to be generated by onshore wind power.

Mike Grubb, who has also done a great deal of detailed research on these issues, puts these figures rather higher. He believes that after taking into account various siting restrictions and economic factors, between 15 per cent and 40 per cent of present electricity demand could be realistically extracted from the British onshore wind energy resource. Grubb calculates that obtaining 10 per cent of present electricity demand from onshore wind would require the building of 1000 arrays of wind machines with heights of 30 metres or 200 arrays of machines 60 metres high.[8] The conclusions of such studies tend to say that the difficulties of finding sites for wind farms are likely to constrain the *rate* of deployment of onshore wind, rather than stopping widespread deployment altogether.

Negotiations with, for example, farmers are likely to take time. They will no doubt hold out in order to secure the best price. Danish and US experience tends to suggest that wind ventures organised by cooperatives or other local bodies encounter fewer misgivings from people living near proposed sites than those organised by remote, centralised or profit-oriented organisations.

The best wind power sites are in windy, hilly areas, and many of these are in Scotland. The best sites are much more economic than coal or nuclear electricity. According to Jackson and Atkinson in their submission to the Hinkley 'C' Enquiry, wind is far more economic than nuclear power at discount rates of 10 per cent, a level which is likely to be close to the rates operating under privatisation (the CEGB operated on a 5 per cent discount rate).

In economic terms, wind power has a big lead over nuclear power, as can be seen from Table 4.2. Many wind sites are also competitive with fossil fuels.

TABLE 4.2: Comparison of generation costs of nuclear power from Sizewell B and from onshore wind at different wind speeds (p/kWh)

Discount Rate:	5%	8%	10%	12%
Wind Speed = 9.8 m/s:	1.79	1.93	2.43	2.71
Wind Speed = 7.6 m/s:	2.45	3.04	3.46	3.91
Sizewell B	3.15	4.26	5.18	6.25

Source: Tim Jackson and Adrian Atkinson, The technical and economic comparison of non-fossil fuelled electricity supply options. Evidence to Hinkley C Inquiry, Hinkley, Somerset, Consortium of Opposing Local Authorities, 1988, pp. 12 and 18.

Estimates of the number of acceptable wind sites with mean annual wind speed of at least 7.6 metres per second vary, but this includes the majority of sites mentioned in, for example, Mike Grubb's estimates of realistically extractable wind resource. It is also to be noted that even with lower wind speeds, the economics of wind compares favourably with nuclear power. This is even more the case if external costs of different types of electricity production are taken into account.

Wind turbines have the advantage that farmers can continue grazing cattle in between the turbines. The idea that wind farms stop the land upon which they are sited from being used for other purposes is a myth. Turbines can be moved with relative ease. Noise pollution becomes negligible at distances over 300 yards. Quieter wind turbines are being developed that should allow deployment at ranges closer than even this. Occasional TV interference can be avoided by building relay transmitter stations, cable networks or by careful siting. Bird deaths are rare. The chances of being killed in a wind generator accident are many, many times smaller than the various hazards associated with fossil or nuclear sources.

At the end of the day some people will still regard wind turbines as an eyesore. The Nature Conservancy Council has expressed fears that the tourist industry could be damaged by wind farms. Yet, as I explained earlier, a comparative environmental impact assessment reveals that the environmental damage resulting from the global warming that would be produced by equivalent fossil fuel plant would surely be many times greater than the alleged visual pollution caused by the wind turbines.

Contributing to global environmental destruction is too high a price to pay for the protection of the view in rural England, especially when the alleged aesthetic disadvantages of wind turbines are largely matters of taste. In fact, estimates of the extent of potential sites made by people like Clarke and Grubb exclude areas of outstanding natural beauty and National Parks. There should be no question of siting wind turbines in such areas.

Some fundamentalist greens object to large scale renewable developments almost as a matter of principle citing the 'small is beautiful' argument. Small is undoubtedly better, but unfortunately in an imperfect world we have to make choices; compromises with industrialism must sometimes be made. Objections to the large-scale deployment of renewable energy sources make no sense at all in a situation where we are churning many millions of tons of carbon dioxide into the atmosphere from fossil fuelled power stations.

Very great efforts should be made to be sensitive to the demands and concerns of local communities, but we should not recoil from championing the cause of wind generators simply because there may be some complaints.

Although we should enthusiastically deploy onshore wind, there are limits to its potential. By the time these limits are reached we should be deploying wind generators on an *offshore* basis. CEGB studies have already identified some offshore sites – mainly in shallow waters off the Norfolk coast – that would, even if only partially exploited, offer a resource comparable to total UK electricity consumption.

The CEGB said that the lower range of the estimated costs

of offshore wind was nearly competitive with conventional electricity sources. On the subject of offshore wind, the CEGB said that 'the technology lies 5–10 years behind onshore wind power and there seems no fundamental reason why it should not become economic if sufficient funds are made available to encourage research to reduce the costs of the rotor, tower, foundation, transmission and maintenance costs.[9] Bearing in mind the fact that the CEGB defined competitiveness in terms of their estimates of electricity from Sizewell B, and considering their much criticised tendencies to understate the costs of nuclear power, these comments seem highly favourable.

In fact offshore wind power already exists in the form of a wind farm off the Mols Peninsular in Jutland, in Denmark. The West Germans and Swedes are actively pursuing plans for offshore wind farms. The UK's offshore wind resources are comparable to total UK electricity consumption, as can be seen in Figure 4.3.

Yet progress in researching offshore wind in the UK is painfully slow. If the political will was there, over 10 per cent of our electricity supply could be provided by wind power by 2010 and, with offshore wind making larger contributions in the following ten years, a total of 25 per cent of electricity demand could be supplied from wind power by the year 2020. Offshore wind could be deployed at a much more rapid rate than onshore wind, since there are no local interests to accommodate. Furthermore, the wind levels and therefore the power outputs from offshore wind parks can be predicted with a certain degree of accuracy, meaning that offshore wind can, per machine, provide a larger amount of equivalent 'firm' power.

A third of electricity could be provided by wind by 2025, a target which would be made easier if the demand for electricity has been reduced by conservation measures. Such a programme would involve considerable investment, but this would be comparable to investing in new conventional fossil stations to replace ageing power stations.

Given the experience of the chaotic 'windrush' in California, there would need to be regulation and government assistance through a Dutch style capital grants system rather than the

OFF-SHORE WIND POWER AREAS
☐ Possible
■ Probable

Figure 4.3: Offshore wind sites in CEGB *feasibility study. [Source Atom, 344, June 1985. Note: the 'probable' wind sites offer a resource approaching the* UK's *total electricity consumption.]*

Californian tax incentive scheme. In Holland grants are only made available for machines which achieve certain standards. A target of 5GW of wind capacity by 2005 is not too adventurous.

Michael Flood estimates that after the first offshore wind parks were deployed, the numbers of offshore wind turbines could be increased quite rapidly to produce more than 60TWh of electricity by 2025.[10]

Because wind is intermittent, like tidal and wave sources, the inefficiency of currently known energy storage systems means that they cannot provide the whole of the electricity supply. However the grid, fed from various sources around the UK, can even out local variations. Electrical engineers such as Mike Grubb calculate that single intermittent renewable sources could provide up to a third of electricity supply without major penalties and that up to 50 per cent could come from a combination of intermittent sources.[11]

If, as I advocate, a larger proportion of electricity came from gas turbines, and fossil fuel stations were small, we would have a much more flexible electricity supply system which could more easily handle very high penetrations from intermittent sources.

Development of effective energy storage systems would greatly assist the long term development of renewable energy sources. Pressurised air, flywheels, batteries, chemicals, waxes, hydrogen from electrolysed water and other types of storage are technologies that should be energetically researched. However, the intermittency argument is not an argument against deployment of renewables since the levels at which this would be a problem are a long way off being reached.

Some renewable sources, like geothermal and biomass, do not suffer from problems of intermittent supply. This means that renewables could, even with current technology, provide well over 50 per cent of the electricity supply. Indeed there is no theoretical, practical or even commercial reason why renewables could not match the two thirds of electricity supply which the nuclear power industry says that it can supply. Besides producing electricity, a source like biomass can produce direct heat. Interest in biomass as an energy source is increasing, and it is to this that I now turn.

BIOMASS

Biomass includes harvested wood crops and wood wastes, land-fill gas, straw, farm animal wastes, sewage and refuse derived fuel.

There is increasing interest in growing wood such as fast-growing willow as an energy crop. Some European Community reports have even suggested that the various biomass sources could provide 10 per cent of Europe's energy by the year 2000. This is probably an overestimate in the short term, but not in the long term.

The use of biocrops for energy purposes makes no net addition to atmospheric carbon dioxide levels, provided of course that the crops are replanted. Since the trees or plants obtain all their carbon from the atmosphere in the first place, burning them does not put more carbon into the atmosphere than was taken out by the biocrop to start with.

The use of biomass wastes for energy purposes also creates an ecological balance. For example, if woodlands are managed properly, a great deal of otherwise waste wood can be burned for energy purposes. If the wood is not burned it still decomposes to produce carbon dioxide. Global warming is reduced by burning other forms of waste. Refuse, left on its own, will produce methane which is many times more powerful in terms of its addition to the greenhouse effect than carbon dioxide.

Over ten per cent of Sweden's primary energy requirements is produced from biomass, although mainly from forestry and other waste material. However in recent years energy forestry, growing trees for energy purposes, has been expanding. Some estimates suggest that Sweden could derive a third of its energy needs from biomass waste alone. In Britain the potential of biomass waste sources is also very considerable. The economics of energy from waste are often very good since the raw material is a by-product of other activities.

A growing number of people are becoming interested in producing electricity from trees. Fast growing trees can be 'coppiced' and burned in small generators to produce electricity which can be fed into the grid. Bernard Wilkins, who is Secretary of the Wood Energy Development Group, says that farmers can make more money from growing trees to produce electricity than they can make from growing cereals.[12] On the basis of his figures it would appear that electricity from trees is competitive with conventional electricity sources even without subsidies.

With more and more farmland becoming surplus to requirements, the potential is enormous. Officially there are around one million hectares of surplus farmland in the UK, while unofficial estimates put this three or four times higher. Derelict land in urban areas would also be a possible site for energy forestry. Wilkins estimates that around 7MTCE will be produced each year from each million hectares of fast growing willow trees. Steve Newman of the Open University says that around 10MTCE per million hectares could be derived from growing poplar trees instead, which could be grown organically. Different strains would be planted thus obviating the need for pesticides. Recycling of residual wood-ash and nitrogen from flue gases could remove the need for artificial fertilisers. Wood produces no sulphur emissions and most if not all nitrogen oxide production could be restrained or scrubbed. Contributions to acid rain would be minimal.

Steve Newman believes that large numbers of farmers could turn to energy forestry if they were given reasonable rates for their electricity. Grants could be given to farmers to enable them to buy generators. There are several types of small generator in use in Sweden. Newman told me that 'all the technology is there; what is needed is a policy to promote it.'[13]

The potential is very great, especially when one takes into account the 3 or 4MTCE that can be derived simply by collecting waste wood through better forest management. Altogether the potential energy forestry resource could be in excess of 30MTCE a year, a lot more than the 20MTCE of primary energy produced from nuclear power in the UK.

Wood crops could be producing 30TWh of electricity by 2025, at commercial rates. This would represent only half the total energy forestry resource. Several MTCE of energy could be produced from energy forestry for heat or heating purposes.

The Department of Energy's Energy Technology Support

Unit (ETSU) have been making good progress in testing furnaces suitable for burning wood to provide factories with heat of various grades. So waste wood and wood crops could be used for other energy purposes apart from making electricity.

Another promising, although not as extensive, biofuel resource is landfill gas. Methane is being produced by rubbish tips as they rot. Not only can this cause explosions, but the methane adds to the greenhouse effect. We can burn the gas to produce energy in the form of direct heat or electricity or better still combined heat and power for industry. In doing so we turn methane, a very potent greenhouse gas, into the less potent carbon dioxide.

ETSU say that energy from landfill gas could rise to 1–3MTCE. Although this is a relatively small energy source, it is still likely to produce around 1 per cent of the UK's energy needs.

Straw, popularised by Prince Charles, has considerable potential too. At present much straw is burned off, causing local as well as global pollution. The straw could provide fuel for boilers and furnaces on farms and in local industry. Over 3MTCE of energy could be produced this way. This potential may not be reached because there are various other ways of disposing of straw (as opposed to burning) that are being canvassed. But it should be remembered that options involving burying the material will act to increase methane production as the straw rots. As I have said, methane is many times more powerful than carbon dioxide in promoting global warming.

There is very large energy potential from refuse derived fuel. Domestic and industrial waste can be formed into pellets and burned. Concern over toxins such as dioxins produced by refuse incineration has led to the European Community setting emission limits. Consequently incinerating plants are being replaced, and the economics of refuse derived fuel are being altered by the need to incorporate flue gas scrubbing devices into burners. Nevertheless, it seems that with increasing opposition to the disposal of wastes via landfill sites, disposal of municipal refuse by incineration is likely to grow, although increasing emphasis also needs to be put on recycling as much waste material as possible.

However, if refuse is going to be burned, then energy should be produced as a by-product. For this reason it is likely that refuse derived fuel will grow in importance as an energy source, particularly if policy measures favour such a development.

A refuse burning power station which will supply thousands of homes with electricity is being built in Lewisham, consuming rubbish produced by 650,000 people living in south-east London. Hot water mains will heat six London council estates. This project has been encouraged by the non-fossil fuel quota that has to be filled by the Area Electricity Board. Refuse derived fuel should be providing at least 5 TWh of electricity and at least 2MTCE of heat.

The production of biogas from animal wastes using anaerobic digestion techniques is another area of development where costs are falling towards levels that allow economic use of the resource. Sewage is another candidate as a source of biogas.

The Department of Energy estimates the total biomass potential to be at least 20MTCE a year.[14] Many would regard this figure as being an underestimate, including the Select Committee on Energy who asked the Department of Energy to re-evaluate their estimates of biomass contributions in the light of the emerging possibilities of energy forestry.

TIDAL POWER

The UK has considerable resources of tidal power, enough in theory to provide more than 15 per cent of current electricity demand. This energy comes from passing tidal water through a generator. A small tidal barrage has been working at La Rance in France for twenty years. In the UK, the biggest and most talked about scheme is the proposed Severn tidal barrage, with other schemes put forward for the Mersey, Solway Firth, Morecambe Bay and numerous other smaller sites.

The Severn and Mersey schemes are likely to be the cheapest, and thus most attention has been focused on them. In fact there have been two proposals for a Severn barrage, the larger of which would be a truly massive undertaking providing some 7 per cent of total UK electricity demand.

Table 4.3: **Comparative tidal scheme performance**

	Barrage length (km)	Annual energy output (TWh)	Cost of energy (p/kWh)
Severn – Inner line	17	12.9	3.7
Severn – Outer line	20	19.7	4.3
Morecambe Bay	16.6	5.4	4.6
Solway Firth	30	10.1	4.9
Dee	9.5	1.3	6.4
Humber	8.3	2.0	7.0
Wash	19.6	4.7	7.2
Thames	9.0	1.3	8.3
Langstone Harbour	0.6	0.5	5.3
Padstow	0.6	0.6	4.2
Hamford Water	3.2	0.4	8.5
Loch Elive	0.4	0.6	11.7
Cromarty Firth	1.4	0.1	11.8
Dovey	1.3	0.5	7.2
Loch Broom	0.5	0.4	13.2
Milford Haven	1.2	0.2	10.0
Mersey	1.8	1.3	3.6

Source: AC Baker, ICE Symposium Paper, October 1986 cited by NATTA Newsletter 59, May/June 1989.

The sheer cost of tidal schemes has been a barrier to their implementation. At the 5 per cent discount rate used by the CEGB when the statistics for Table 4.3 were drawn up, electricity from the cheapest scheme would cost under 4p/kWh, but if finance is raised on the market under privatisation the costs of even the cheaper schemes could be 8 to 10p/kWh.

Tidal power would be much more expensive than electricity from fossil fuels, although not dearer than nuclear electricity if the likely cost of decommissioning nuclear power stations is taken into account. It seems very unlikely that the tidal schemes would be built totally from private money. There are some fears that the schemes could be put out of action in a few decades by rising sea levels induced by global warming, but such rises would have to be very rapid and very large. The probability that the barrages will last over a century counts for very little with private investors since returns on capital, say, forty or fifty years in the future will be heavily discounted. However, supporters of tidal power argue that nations must have much longer time horizons than private investors and that since long-life tidal barrages will benefit the nation, they ought to be supported by large public investments.

More worrying to greens are the environmental issues. Although tidal schemes will produce 'clean' power once they are going, there will be disruption while the infrastructure needed by the schemes is developed, and wildlife will be disturbed.

In the case of the Severn project, environmentalist groups have complained of the incursions into Sites of Special Scientific Interest (SSSIs). Large developments including a road network would be created as part of the project. The disturbances would be rather greater in the larger version of the scheme; mud flats would be exposed for a reduced period meaning that birds would have to go elsewhere. The Royal Society for the Protection of Birds says many of them would perish. Fish could also be harmed as water passes through the turbines.

Others, favouring deployment, have replied that greater sunlight penetration caused by reduced flow rates would benefit other species. It is also argued that the environmental impact is not in the same league as a large hydro scheme. One advantage of installing tidal schemes is that they would force the authorities to treat sewage rather than dumping it in the river estuaries.

In green terms, the argument against at least the largest tidal projects would be much stronger if it were not for the problem of global warming. In an energy efficient economy we are still going to need considerable quantities of energy that must come from non-fossil sources. If fossil fuels are used instead of tidal power then global warming – which will cause mass species extinctions of birds, other animals, and plants and do untold damage to humanity – will be exacerbated.

It is inconsistent to acquiesce in the construction of fossil fuel plants of whatever type while at the same time actively opposing tidal power schemes, unless it can be demonstrated that investing in tidal power will reduce investment in other forms of renewable energy sources.

The SERA Energy Group believes that public inquiries should be organised to consider the proposals for tidal barrages on the Severn and the Mersey with a view to constructing the Mersey project first, provided there is a favourable outcome from the inquiry. I think that local referendums should be held to take final decisions about proposals for tidal barrages.

HYDROELECTRIC POWER

Currently hydro power supplies just under 2 per cent of UK electricity, most of this coming from Scotland. There is also about 2GW of pumped storage capacity in Wales which gives the electricity system greater flexibility.

The only way hydro power can be expanded without incurring considerable political opposition is through micro-hydro systems, which are very cheap sources of electricity. There are many sites where this can be applied, but it is unlikely that this will greatly increase hydro's share of electricity supply.

It might be possible to create more hydro power storage capacity like the recently opened 2GW Dinorwic plant, which has been built inside a mountain. This would certainly increase the flexibility of the electricity supply system and make it able to absorb higher levels of intermittent renewable supplies, but there are big constraints on the availability of sites.

WAVE POWER

In theory wave power could easily supply the UK's electricity needs. Wave power projects would need to be sited so as to avoid major shipping lanes. Michael Flood estimated that wave power could, in practical terms, supply around 120 MTCE of power.[15]

The attractiveness of wave power is enhanced by the fact that energy from the waves is available in greatest quantities during the winter, precisely when UK energy demand is at its height. However, as yet the only working prototypes of wave machines are for use inshore rather than 'deep sea' where really large resources are available.

Interest in wave power first grew in the wake of the first oil crisis when the government 'think tank' headed by Lord Rothschild presented a wave power scheme that became known as 'Salter's Ducks'. Britain's small wave power research programme was scrapped in 1982 amid complaints from Professor Salter's team that their costings had been misrepresented by a government report. British wave power research has only been revived on a very small level after Norwegian progress on inshore wave power. As most European countries have little interest in wave power, it is up to Britain to take the lead in developing this resource of immense potential.

The inshore devices, which are quite well developed, are likely to produce useful supplies to Scottish coastal communities, but this will make little impact on national energy requirements. Various offshore and onshore systems have been proposed going under names like the Sea Clam, the Oscillating Water Column and the Frog. The Oscillating Water Column appears to show the biggest promise at this stage. Such projects ought to be receiving massive state backing.

It is a sad reflection on priorities that while wave power struggles to obtain any research funding at all fusion power has been bankrolled with tens of millions of pounds a year for decades. Yet the engineering problems associated with wave power are many times less daunting than those associated with nuclear fusion.

GEOTHERMAL ENERGY

Geothermal energy can come in two forms, 'wet' and 'dry'.

The wet form is deployed by many countries around the globe

who use hot water from volcanic activity to produce electricity and provide space heating. Such resources are limited in the UK.

Hot dry rock geothermal energy, however, has very large potential in the UK, as is the case elsewhere. It works by pumping water deep underground through fractured rock formations. The temperature of rock increases with depth by an average of about 30°C per kilometre. The deeper the water is pumped underground, the hotter it will be when it returns to the surface. If water is pumped to a sufficient depth steam can return to the surface to be used to generate electricity, although the bulk of energy supplied from hot dry rock geothermal energy is likely to be used for space heating or water heating purposes.

Evidence to the House of Lords enquiry into alternative energy sources suggested that hot dry rock geothermal energy could, economically, supply 10–15 per cent of UK annual energy requirements.

Prototype plant has been developed in the US and is awaiting commercial take-up. A Utah scheme was in 1986 projected to produce electricity at rates competitive with coal and oil. In the end it was abandoned after a scheme to produce electricity from natural 'wet' geothermal energy from the same site was considered to be even cheaper. Economically recoverable US resources of hot dry rock geothermal energy have been estimated to amount to four thousand times the total annual US energy consumption.[16]

Research work in Cornwall is hampered by a legal wrangle over who has the right to energy from underground and by a lack of interest from both the private and public sectors. Clearly there is a woeful lack of political will to overcome such difficulties.

Given sufficient will and state support, hot dry rock geothermal energy can be deployed in the near future giving electricity and local heat, starting in places like Cornwall and Cumbria. If it is given sufficient backing it should be providing at least 2 per cent of UK primary energy by 2025, the main limitation being the rate at which drilling could take place.

Environmental impacts are likely to be slight.

SOLAR POWER

The biggest source of solar power in this country will be, for the forseeable future, passive solar energy. This is sometimes counted as part of energy conservation. It involves designing buildings so that they take maximum advantage of sunlight. Large south facing windows and conservatories are the most effective ways of capturing passive solar energy.

Solar water heaters seemed to be increasing in popularity up to a few years ago, but falling energy prices have eroded their economic position. They are now only economic in this country if they are fitted on a DIY basis. This is a far cry from the position in rather warmer California, where solar heaters have to be fitted as a condition of house sales.

In recent times solar water heaters have encountered another problem in that legionnaires disease can develop in the system, since in this country the solar heaters do not heat the water to a high enough temperature to kill the microbes. Thus solar heaters can only safely be used in conjunction with conventional heaters, although in practice solar heating is generally used in conjunction with other heating, such as pre-heating for gas heating.

We should not write off solar heating altogether since its economic competitiveness is after all in the same range as double glazing. Both solar heating and double glazing are much more cheaply installed at the construction stage.

Solar heaters may still provide useful energy if building regulations stipulate that new houses must include solar heating. Solar heated water will be more economic for domestic and even industrial uses if fossil fuel energy prices are put up by heavy rates of energy taxation.

Electricity can be derived from solar photovoltaics. The technology is advancing fast; it will not be long before it will be a significant energy source in warmer climates. It is not as yet economic in the UK except in marginal uses like calculators to replace high cost and extremely wasteful batteries.

Nevertheless, solar photovoltaics is a very young technology which emerged in the 1960s as a result of the US space programme. Bearing in mind the rate of recent advances in solar power technology, and the fact that current energy pricing regimes do not take into account external costs of energy sources, we should not rule out the possibility that solar photovoltaics may have considerable potential in the UK as early as the beginning of the next century.

In California there is an increasing quantity of electricity generated from solar heated water and photovoltaics. Photovoltaic rooftiles are being developed in Japan and West Germany. If such technology is developed to the point where it can be cost-effectively deployed, as seems more than possible, 'rooftop' photovoltaics would produce considerable reductions in the demand for grid-supplied electricity.

Solar power has, for decades if not centuries, been seen as the energy source of the future. Today, with the advances being made in photovoltaics and even solar cars, that future does not seem too far removed. However, in the near and medium term future this country's main renewable sources are likely to be wind, biomass, tidal, geothermal and given a major research initiative, perhaps wave power.

I shall now illustrate what the UK's energy future might be if we follow a sustainable path prioritising energy conservation and deployment of renewable energy sources.

The strategies I have advocated in this book do not point to a single outcome. There is a range of outcomes, including differing degrees of energy conservation and combinations of renewable energy sources. Let us see what some of these combinations could be.

5 Energy Futures

In order to illustrate the sort of outcomes that flow from the policies already described I have elaborated two scenarios. This does not imply a 'one or other' choice. A number of different combinations are possible, and the two scenarios are meant merely to illustrate some of the possibilities, not to make predictions.

I have named the two scenarios 'moderate' and 'radical'. They illustrate different levels and mixes of UK primary energy consumption in 2025. The 'radical' scenario assumes that our activities become as energy efficient as is technically possible by 2025. The 'moderate' scenario also assumes high levels of energy efficiency, but below what is technically achievable.

The scenarios are based loosely on the projections of delivered energy contained in the two so-called 'technical fix' scenarios elaborated in Olivier's *Energy Efficient Futures*. I have not used Olivier's supply side projections as they are to some extent speculative and dependent upon high fossil fuel prices. Thus the supply side figures making up the energy scenarios mentioned in Tables 5.1 and 5.2 are my own, although the overall totals of primary UK energy consumption are similar to the two scenarios described by Olivier, which assumed overall rates of economic growth of 2.2 per cent per annum. This is similar to those achieved in the UK in the 1970s and 1980s.

Both scenarios are radical in the sense that they assume much higher rates of energy conservation and quantities of renewable energy than are conventionally accepted. They are also non-nuclear.

THE 'MODERATE' SCENARIO

This scenario[1] assumes that very good progress has been made towards achieving the super-efficient building insulation standards described earlier, and that the bulk of old houses have been comprehensively retrofitted.

Motor car fuel efficiencies have been increased by around 60 per cent, there has been widespread adoption of industrial CHP schemes, and approaching half of domestic lighting is provided by fluorescent strips or lamps. The average efficiency of electrical appliances approaches the best possible efficiencies of current models. Services take up a much greater proportion of gross domestic product while industry is two or three times as energy efficient as today.

In this scenario UK energy consumption is reduced by around 32 per cent of its 1987 level, and carbon dioxide production is reduced by around 47 per cent compared to 1987. Renewable energy's proportion of total energy climbs to about 25 per cent. See Table 5.1.

There is widespread substitution of coal by natural gas, although coal is still used extensively in industry and in electricity production via fluidised bed combustion. Despite the relative substitution of coal by gas, the quantity of gas consumed is still far less than was the case in 1987.

The quantities of energy projected from the four biggest renewable sources – wind, biomass, geothermal and tidal power – are well short of their likely economic potential.

Tidal power is included in this scenario. Many greens feel that there are sufficient alternative renewable sources to forego large-scale tidal power deployment. However, early deployment of tidal power would have the advantage of building up renewable sources very considerably by the year 2005. This in turn should strengthen the case for an early phase-out of nuclear power.

Tim Jackson and Adrian Atkinson's scenarios of the build-up of renewables between 2000 and 2010 (see Figures 5.1 and 5.2) include the Severn barrage only as a delayed optional extra. They estimate that, excluding the Severn barrage, renewables can by

Table 5.1 Shares of UK primary energy consumption in 'moderate scenario (PJ)

	1987	2025	
Coal	3020	1245	
Oil	3375	2125	One MTCE is taken
Gas	2243	1365	to equal 26.4PJ.
Nuclear	525	—	
Renewables	54	1545	
Total	9217	6280	

The contribution from renewables (PJ)

	Heat supplied or fuel saved (PJ)[2]
Wind (onshore and offshore)	650
Tidal	150
Wave	5
Hydro	55
Geothermal	200
Biofuels	425
Solar	60
Total	1545

2010 be providing 34TWh of electricity (equivalent to roughly 360PJ) Putting the Severn barrage on line would increase this amount to approaching 50TWh.[3]

Jackson and Atkinson's scenarios are on the conservative side since they do not make allowance for the recent upsurge in interest in energy forestry, which could easily double the quantity of electricity from biomass shown in their scenarios by the year 2010.

THE 'RADICAL' SCENARIO

This scenario[4] assumes very high deployment of the most efficient types of currently available technology, 55 per cent of industrial electricity is produced by industrial CHP plant, and cars are twice as energy efficient as at present, although car use

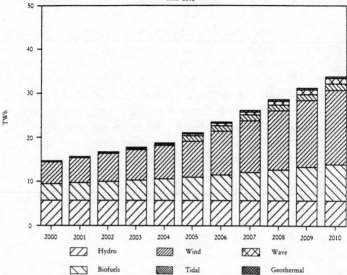

2000–2010

Figure 5.1: Renewables programme (Jackson and Atkinson)

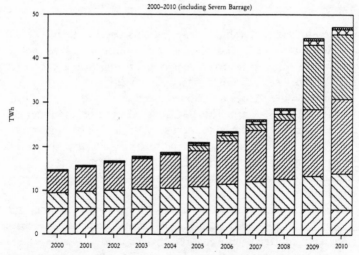

Figure 5.2: Renewables programme (Jackson and Atkinson) [Source: T. Jackson and A. Atkinson, The Technical and Economic Comparison of non-fossil fuelled electricity supply options. *Evidence to Hinkley 'C' Enquiry, Hinkley Consortium of Opposing Local Authorities, 1988, p. 80).*

expands. Fluorescent lighting provides all lighting, including in the domestic sector.

Electricity provides only 6 per cent of delivered energy, under half the 1987 proportion, and there is a very extensive substitution of coal by natural gas in both the industrial and electrical production sectors. The shares of primary energy consumption in 2025 are shown in Table 5.2, and represent a nearly 47 per cent reduction in energy consumption compared to 1987. Carbon dioxide emissions are reduced by over 61 per cent.

Table 5.2: Shares of UK primary energy in the 'Radical' scenario (PJ)	
Coal	660
Oil	1620
Gas	1320
Nuclear	–
Renewables	1300
Total	4900

There is less renewable energy in this scenario because of the drastically reduced level of electricity consumption. Nevertheless renewables take up nearly 27 per cent of total primary energy, slightly more than in the 'moderate' scenario.

Many people would question the practicality of the 'radical' scenario. They can argue that what is technically possible may not be practically achievable because of the length of time equipment and housing take to be replaced, or because very high levels of energy taxation or oil crisis induced price rises would be needed to encourage such high rates of investment in energy efficiency.

It is true that progress in energy efficiency takes time, but within a 30 to 40 year period most capital items can be cost-effectively replaced with energy efficient models – except perhaps for buildings, and these can be extensively retrofitted.

Many, if not most, of the energy savings can be achieved independently of rises in the price of energy. The scenario does illustrate that high levels of carbon dioxide abatement can be achieved alongside improvements in consumer services and econ-

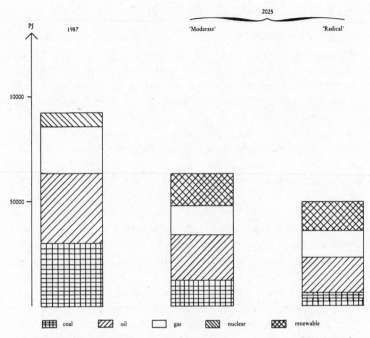

Figure 5.3: UK primary energy consumption, present and projected.

omic growth, provided that the drive for energy efficiency is backed by energetic legislative and fiscal action.

However the fact that high energy prices have encouraged greater efficiency in the past means that we must seriously consider energy taxation policies, especially as energy taxation can also be used to encourage take-up of renewable energy sources and to generate income for conservation programmes. Energy taxation does have social ramifications, and I shall consider these in the chapter dealing with political means.

The 'radical' scenario may underestimate the pace of development in energy efficient technologies. It may also underestimate the degree to which economic growth switches away from energy intensive goods towards light industry and services. The size of future energy demand is thus bound up with not only the size but also the nature of economic growth.

THE FUTURE SHAPE OF GROWTH

Overall, a sustainable economic strategy will involve growth in light industry and services which use little energy and no or little growth in heavy industries and goods which encourage consumption of large amounts of energy. For example, we should see more spending on leisure and education and less on cars and road building.

If instead of spending more money on cars and petrol, I spend more money on eating in a restaurant, staying in a hotel, or taking up an educational course, I will probably be using little more, and perhaps even less energy, then if I stayed at home. Yet my standard of living would have increased. My extra consumption of services would have contributed to sustainable growth, whereas spending on cars and petrol would have been unsustainable.

If we can achieve this type of growth in the context of reducing energy consumption and shifting to renewable sources of energy, then we can increase our living standards in a sustainable fashion.

The most important issue of green economics is not whether we achieve zero economic growth, in terms of gross domestic product, but whether we are reducing pollution and resource depletion by cutting out waste and increasing reliance on renewable and recycled resources.

The notion that there is an indissoluble link between a given level of national income and a given level of energy consumption is erroneous, as is demonstrated by the statistics in Table 5.3.

The average citizen of the Soviet Union uses 57 per cent more energy than the average Japanese, yet receives less than half the income of the average Japanese citizen. This comparison illustrates very clearly that lower levels of income do not necessarily mean lower levels of energy consumption.

Furthermore, the statistics demonstrate how the USA and the UK lag well behind Denmark and Japan in the energy efficiency stakes. The latter two nations have much higher energy prices and are much more reliant on imported energy than the UK or the USA.

It is clear from the table that the Chinese must be helped to

Table 5.3: Comparison of income and energy consumption in six countries

Country	Per capita national income ($)	Per capita energy consumption (kgce)	Energy/income ratio (kgce per $)
Denmark	9709	4521	0.47
UK	7156	4760	0.67
USSR	4200	5977	1.42
USA	14565	9577	0.66
Japan	9542	3800	0.40
China	270	664	2.45

Note: kgce stand for kilograms of coal equivalent

Source: The World in Figures, London, The Economist Publications Ltd., 1987, p. 13. The energy figures are for 1984 and the national incomes are for 1985.

make their economy much more energy efficient. They have immense reserves of coal, and if they follow the same over productionist path already trod by the USSR, the effect on the ecosphere will be catastrophic.

Often the dark green attachment to 'no growth' is taken by critics to mean that they are against providing more jobs, something that deeply alienates trade unionists. Yet this is not what greens mean. They want growth in employment, but in areas that will not lead to unsustainable demands on resources or increased levels of pollution. For example, instead of creating jobs through road building programmes that ruin the environment we should spend more on areas like education which will also create new jobs – for teachers, school cleaners, and others.

We can choose to increase our standards of living through redirecting our economic activities along sustainable lines. We shall continue to need some heavy industry, but it must be made much more energy and resource efficient. Increasing industrial production can only be sustainably achieved if it is done while reducing the total amount of energy and resources consumed both in the production process and by the products themselves when they are put to use.

On the basis of the preceding analysis, a strategy involving sustainable growth could enable us to reduce carbon dioxide emissions by around three-fifths of 1987 levels by the year 2025, and by up to a quarter by 2005, while phasing out nuclear power in the process. The Association for the Conservation of Energy has estimated that carbon dioxide emissions can be reduced by 20 per cent by 2005 through energy efficiency measures on the basis of an economic growth rate of 2.5 per cent per annum.[5]

All of this cannot be achieved in a political vacuum. We need political structures that will help implement this strategy and political vehicles that will propel people committed to sustainable policies into office.

Before concluding this book I shall sketch some of the political structures needed for a sustainable energy policy, and discuss the political vehicles required by such a strategy.

6 Political Means

POLITICAL STRUCTURES

An energy policy is a political necessity for any government. The interests of both the consumer and the environment cannot be served without one.

Energy policy and energy planning must be oriented towards giving consumers a good service through the efficient use of less energy rather than the wasteful supply of more. The role of the Energy Efficiency Office will be crucial in this process. However the Energy Efficiency Office must have a massively upgraded set of functions and powers and a big budget at its disposal. The Energy Efficiency Office should have control over the domestic energy conservation and public buildings insulation programmes. It should be responsible for the national heat board which would be responsible for supplying finance to local energy utilities to develop district heating and CHP schemes. The Energy Efficiency Office would also have its own energy efficiency inspectorate. The Building Research Establishment should be brought under the same roof as the Energy Efficiency Office.

At the moment responsibilities for energy conservation are divided between the Departments of Energy, Environment and (on paper only) Transport. They should be put under one roof.

In order to ensure that environmental priorities were properly integrated with energy policy making it would be necessary to set up a cabinet committee consisting of environment, energy and other ministers with the specific remit to deal with energy and the environment.

If there is a much stronger and well financed Energy Efficiency

Office and if the electricity supply industry is municipalised then the consumer and the conservation interest will be stronger in a reshaped Department of Energy that promotes increasing supply of renewable sources of energy but conservation of the rest.

It is important that the Energy Efficiency Office has the biggest say in the drafting of a national energy plan. It should also have responsibility for monitoring the progress of local energy plans drawn up by local energy utilities in collaboration with local government, and for guiding the local utilities towards targets set by a national energy plan. This type of energy planning is done in Sweden.

Swedish experience demonstrates that it is possible to combine national planning with a decentralised structure of government. Indeed national planning will be more effective if local people have more power since it is only they who know how to achieve nationally set objectives in local circumstances. National planning should be done by setting targets, monitoring their achievement, creating the right structures, and guiding the market by use of appropriate fiscal and regulatory policies.

Efforts to implement combined heat and power and district heating (CHP/DH) schemes in countries such as Denmark, West Germany and Sweden suggest that a decentralised electricity supply industry including heavy local authority involvement is essential for serious progress to be made in such ventures. The Science Policy Research Unit has briefly described how local authority involvement is important to energy conservation at a local level.[1] Adrian Atkinson described various ways in which local government could organise CHP/DH schemes.[2]

The conditions obtaining either under a centralised public – or the still largely centralised privatised – electricity supply industry will not favour CHP/DH, the deployment of which is essential if the interests of both the consumer and the environment are to be served well. Unless the distribution, if not the generation, of electricity is wholly in the hands of local utilities local government will be at a permanent disadvantage in negotiations with electricity generating companies whose own interests do not include assisting the development of co-generation schemes.

Both socialist and ecological objectives could be achieved by municipalising the electricity supply system. Responsibility for the distribution of electricity as well as heat supplies should be given to local energy utilities. These utilities could be organised in several different ways. Two of the most promising are 'mixed' ownership and ownership by 'consumer co-operatives'. Mixed ownership would still (preferably) involve majority municipal control, to ensure public accountability, with local authorities having a 51 per cent stake in the utilities. The rest of the shares could be bought by local industry with an interest in selling energy to or buying it from the municipal energy utilities.

Another and even more democratic way would be to set up the local utilities as consumer co-operatives. A board would be elected by the consumers, which would in turn appoint the management. A radical restructuring of utilities could involve giving local consumer co-operatives control of other services such as water.

Municipal control of heat and power distribution would create a much more attractive environment for combined heat and power, investment in energy efficiency and the exploitation of local renewable energy resources than exists at the moment.

The geographical boundaries of local utilities should mirror those of local government so that CHP schemes could be developed to dovetail with local authority housing schemes and planning policies. Contracts for the installation of the CHP/DH schemes would be put out to tender by the distribution utilities. Independent electricity generators would be able to compete with others through this system.

Such a strategy would mean that the local economy would benefit through improved housing provision and also in new jobs, not only in laying the infrastructure of the systems, but also in maintaining them once installed.

The 1979 Marshall Report advocated the setting up of a national heat board to develop CHP/district heating schemes. Regardless of whether energy services are municipalised a national heat board would be needed to provide low interest loans. The national heat board's investment fund could come from energy taxation. Municipal authorities should be required by law to prepare plans for, first, district heating and then CHP schemes which could be assessed by the national heat board.

The existing generation side of the electricity industry, which after the power sell-off consists mostly of PowerGen and National Power, should be decentralised along with the distribution side. Nationally oriented generating companies concentrate on remote, large generating units. This leads to transmission losses because of the remoteness from the point of delivery of electricity. It also leads to reductions in the flexibility of the system to respond to short-term variations in electricity demand and plant breakdowns compared to a system consisting of smaller, faster responding, units.

Crucially, the overriding concern of remote, centralised electricity systems to produce electricity efficiently supercedes the objective of making the most efficient use of energy by reducing conversion losses.

The two dominant generating concerns PowerGen and National Power should be split up, perhaps on regional lines, as recommended by the Science Policy Research Unit. The regionally based generating companies could each be owned by a consortium of the local utilities in their region. The national grid should have responsibility for the security of supply and this could be owned either by a grand consortium of the municipal distributors or be run as a traditional public corporation.

The electricity systems in Denmark, Sweden and West Germany are to a greater or lesser extent based on municipal or mixed patterns of control. The higher the level of municipal control, the higher is the proportion of profits from electricity and heat production that can be ploughed back into local services.

A decentralised, integrated energy supply industry based on social ownership is much more likely to benefit the consumer and the environment, as well as promoting competition and technological diversity, than a still largely centralised, producer dominated and privatised electricity supply industry.

The electricity utilities should be required by law to apply integrated least cost planning to their activities to ensure that investment in energy conservation is applied where it is cheaper

PEOPLE POWER

Figure 6.1

than investment in new generating capacity. A powerful national regulatory commission should ensure that least cost planning techniques are properly implemented and that independent electricity generators are paid fair rates for their electricity.

On the supply side, the idea of the non-fossil fuel quota is one positive idea to have come out of electricity privatisation. It could, in a different form, be used to advance the interests of renewables. Since the 1950s a policy of giving a strategic and privileged position to nuclear power has been almost taken for granted. The 20 per cent non-fossil fuel quota was intended to continue this policy under privatisation. The costs of supplying the non-fossil fuel quota would be paid for by higher prices through the non-fossil fuel levy.

Environmental and even security considerations should demand that renewables be given strategic institutionalised support. After all, combatting pollution is a non-market objective and we must intervene in the market to ensure that renewable energy sources are favoured more than fossil fuels. The government has already conceded that renewables should have their own 'quota' of 600MW of 'firm' capacity by the year 2000.

The SERA Energy Group believes this is much too cautious and calls for a quota of 2GW of wind, 2GW of biomass, 500MW of micro hydro and 600MW of tidal capacity to be constructed by the year 2000. The electricity supply industry should be required to meet 25 per cent of electricity supply from renewables by the year 2010.

This quota could be raised in stages to sixty per cent or even two thirds by the year 2025. The further development of biomass, solar, wave and geothermal energy sources could mean that even higher proportions of electricity and large amounts of heat could be supplied from renewable energy sources.

Even if the idea of making energy utilities fulfil quotas proves impractical, the government could still set targets, and gear subsidies and taxation policies towards achieving such targets.

Existing independent electricity producers have been charged higher local government rates than power stations owned by the CEGB and their successor companies; this absurd set of priorities must be reversed. Co-generators and producers of renewable energy should be charged lower rates than fossil fuel or nuclear power stations.

Financial incentives, including the Dutch type of capital grants, should be given to renewable energy producers. This system of capital grants could be combined with a system whereby the government gave an allowance to renewable producers for each unit of electricity sold to the utilities. This could have the effect of giving the producers an extra incentive to improve the performance of their operations.

The industry should be regulated to ensure that renewable energy producers receive good prices for their electricity. US style legislation which aims to ensure that independents are paid according to the long term avoided cost principle should be urgently adopted in the UK.

A moratorium should be declared on power station construction by the existing generating establishment. The privatisation proposals gave National Power and PowerGen control over the most suitable power stations sites; independents should now be allowed access to such sites.

Independent electricity producers should also be able to compete for contracts to supply all industrial consumers. The agreement between the government and the generating duopoly said that only they could supply industrial customers of less than 1MW with power for the first five years.

The levying of 'carbon' and 'nuclear' taxes would also benefit renewables by promoting fuel switching to renewable sources.

A renewable energy authority should be created as the major centre for research into energy provision. The Energy Technology Support Unit should be split away from the UK Atomic Energy Authority and put under the aegis of the new authority.

Renewable energy research should be receiving at least the £200 million per year the nuclear industry has received in the past. The UK Atomic Energy Authority could be given residual funds for research into disposal of nuclear waste and the decommissioning of power stations to support a programme of phasing out nuclear power.

The renewable energy authority could issue licences to municipally controlled regional generating companies or consortia of generating companies to develop, for example, offshore wind programmes to fulfil renewable energy quotas.

The Department of Energy should develop a bias towards renewable energy sources.

One increasingly talked about means of encouraging fuel switching to renewable energy sources and also of inducing energy efficiency is that of altering energy prices through energy taxation. It is problematic and controversial and needs to be considered as a separate issue.

ENERGY PRICING AND TAXATION POLICY

Many people are suggesting that internationally agreed levels of energy taxation should be levied so that the international environmental consequences of energy consumption are reflected in the price of energy. In particular various calls have been made for a 'carbon tax' to be levied on fossil fuels in proportion to their emissions of carbon dioxide. A 'nuclear tax' could also be levied to take account of the international consequences of nuclear accidents as well as the more intangible military and security problems posed by nuclear power.

It would be impractical (at least in the forseeable future) for such taxation to be implemented through a single global system, but given the political will, there is no reason why the major industrial nations should not agree to set generally agreed taxation levels within their own boundaries. The European Community is in a good position to levy such taxes.

In a paper to the 1989 Turin climate conference Ernst von Weizsacker proposed energy taxation levels of 200 per cent. He said that without punitively high energy taxation there would not be enough pressure for fuel switching and energy efficiency improvements to ensure that carbon dioxide abatement targets were met. He rejected the notion that such measures would necessarily make the countries that introduced them uncompetitive in industrial terms. He said that such results could be avoided:

> A tax on all energy consumption means income for the state; that income can theoretically be returned to the private sector by a more or less equivalent reduction of other taxes ... The basic idea is to eventually shift a considerable part of the tax burden from labour value added and capital to energy resources and pollution. Taxation of labour and capital will be reduced approximately by the amount of energy, resources and pollution taxes, so that the average tax burden on industry is not increased ... [3]

Weizsacker went on to say that such taxation would have the attraction of being difficult to evade. It would also have the effect of penalising energy intensive industries while favouring industries that used little energy.

It is possible that in ten years' time such ideas will not be regarded as unusual, especially if regulatory devices fail to deliver sufficiently large amounts of energy conservation. Nevertheless high rates of energy taxation could not be introduced overnight. Neither could they be justified without introducing means to counteract what would otherwise be very inegalitarian consequences. The Green Party, whose own ideas favour a shift to energy and resource taxation, wants a universally applicable 'basic income scheme.'

High levels of energy taxation, in the form of carbon and nuclear taxes, would have three effects. First, they would give a powerful boost to renewable energy sources which are, in several cases, already economically attractive.

Second, they would be a strong inducement to use energy more efficiently, especially in the short term, for the short-term effect would be mainly to increase energy prices since it would take time for renewable sources to provide a major portion of energy supply.

Third, such taxation would make available considerable tax receipts which could contribute towards an environmental protection fund. This could, among other things, finance energy conservation programmes, grants to producers of renewable energy, and international aid. Energy taxation should also be used to fund extra income support for those who would otherwise be hard hit by rising energy prices.

Although an increasing emphasis on energy taxation seems inevitable it would be wrong to imagine that, on their own, energy taxes represent a complete answer to our problems.

In the domestic sector of the energy market energy savings would result not only from improvements in energy efficiency but also from hardship caused by the creation of energy shortages with people not being able to keep themselves warm. Indeed people on low incomes could miss out on energy conservation opportunities by not being able to afford the capital investment in, say, home insulation.

Thus as a greater proportion of tax revenue is raised through energy taxation and resource taxation, measures have to be implemented to help people who would otherwise suffer hardship because of higher prices. The Green Party's basic income scheme is designed to remedy this sort of situation. A more modest variant could be to give everyone, as of right, an energy allowance. Universal benefits should be raised, including state pensions and social security. Personal tax allowances should be raised and the income tax system, which would deliver a reduced proportion of total tax revenue, should be made more progressive in nature.

People facing hardship should be given 100 per cent grants for home insulation and cheap, efficient heating systems and grants for replacing old inefficient electrical appliances with new more efficient models. The best long term solution for fuel poverty is the provision of district heating.

The abolition of standing charges for gas, electricity and district heating and bringing in inverted energy tariffs would encourage energy efficiency. Inverted tariffs mean that the first units of energy consumed are charged at a low rate. The more energy is consumed, the higher will be the unit prices charged. Indeed such a system is more likely to induce energy efficiency than flat rate systems. An inverted tariff system will mean higher prices for the larger industrial users, and it is in the industrial rather than the domestic or commercial sectors where a high energy price policy is likely to produce the most gains in energy efficiency. At the moment bulk users of electricity actually pay less, kilowatt for kilowatt, than smaller domestic users. The first effective step would therefore be to charge electricity at a flat rate.

Consumers would be encouraged by high energy prices to look for energy efficient appliances, but it should be apparent from my preceding analysis of energy conservation opportunities that probably even greater gains could come from setting energy efficiency standards for appliances, from tightening up insulation standards in building regulations, and from making home insulation universally available at low or even zero cost.

In some parts of the energy market, such as the commercial sector, energy price rises would have little effect, unless they were raised several times over. Commercial rents are often hundreds of times larger than energy bills. In this sector most of the energy savings would come from stringent energy efficiency standards rather than higher energy prices.

Energy taxation would be more effective in inducing greater efficiency in the transport sector. Public transport and pedal power are much more energy efficient and generally more environmentally benign than private motor transport. The price of petrol should be doubled, in real terms, through a series of increases in petrol taxation, and road pricing schemes should be introduced. Motor vehicle taxation should be re-arranged to reward fuel efficiency. Putting up the price of private motorised transport would not produce hardship provided public transport was subsidised and cycle facilities improved as an alternative.

Although consolidated motor car taxation in the UK is much heavier than in the USA and West Germany, it is still 10 per cent less than in France and Japan for the average 1500cc car.[4]

Alistair Ulph and Alan Ingham, economists at Southampton University, tell me that carbon taxes of 170 per cent for coal (and pro rata, according to carbon content) for oil and gas would be needed to cut carbon dioxide emissions from the industrial sector by 20 per cent by 2005. The taxes would be phased in.

Energy and resource taxation will not reduce economic growth. Taxation will shift production to less energy intensive goods and services. Ulph and Ingham's econometric model suggests that carbon taxes would increase output and employment because firms would invest in new energy efficient equipment and substitute labour for energy inputs. However, even in the sectors where higher prices will be effective in inducing energy efficiency, standards (e.g. to improve motor vehicle fuel efficiency) and regulation will be very important, not to mention tax breaks and subsidies of various sorts. I have already detailed many such stratagems.

So how should we, in practical terms, start to implement an energy taxation policy?

We should start by ensuring that subsidies and tariff arrangements which encourage energy consumption are ended. Anomalies such as the levying of VAT on energy conservation measures while energy consumption is zero rated should also be abolished. In some countries VAT is charged on energy consumption. The European Community may soon put VAT on energy.

We might learn from the Danes who kept their energy prices, in real terms, at 1985 levels despite the fall in world energy prices in recent years. In 1987 10 per cent of Danish tax revenue was obtained from energy taxes. We should ensure that tariffs penalise profligate consumption of energy in the industrial sector.

A carbon tax could be levied on consumption of fossil fuels in proportion to the carbon content of each fossil fuel. If this tax were levied in such a way that the price of coal increased by 50 per cent, approaching £3,300 million would have been raised in 1987 from carbon taxes in the UK assuming that the demand for fossil fuels remained the same as it was without the tax. In fact this is likely to be the case at first, as it would take time before the renewable energy supplies were deployed. It is unlikely that taxation at lower rates would lead to much fuel switching.

It is argued by many, including UK energy ministers, that we should desist from implementing energy taxation schemes until there is international agreement, because putting up domestic energy prices would damage the competitiveness of British industry. Yet moderate levels of energy taxation would have very little impact on our competitive position and would increase industrial prices by only 1 to 2 per cent. Japan's energy prices are double those faced by UK industry, but this does not appear to disadvantage the Japanese.

Although international agreement, starting in the European Community, on energy taxation is very important, this ought not to rule out unilateral action by the UK to levy a moderate level of energy taxation. If the UK takes the initiative on energy taxation it would put pressure on the European Community to implement it at a higher rate on a European-wide basis.

Two steps ought to be taken in the short term. First, VAT should be levied on electricity and gas consumption. Assuming 1987 levels of expenditure on these fuels, this would raise some £2,750 million. Second, a 10 per cent carbon tax plus an equivalent levy on nuclear electricity would raise at least £350 million. This £3,100 million per annum total of energy taxation receipts could, for example, be disbursed as shown in Table 6.1.

It is likely that it will be rather easier, in political terms, to raise money for these purposes by taxing the very goods that are producing the pollution rather than simply by increasing

Table 6.1: Distribution of monies from environmental protection fund	
Domestic energy conservation programme	£1,000 million
Funding of CHP and district heating development through the national heat board	£800 million
Grants to local authorities for conservation	£250 million
Funding of research into, and subsidies to producers of, renewable energy sources	£800 million
Contribution to international climate protection fund	£250 million

income tax. Opinion poll evidence suggests that people would support this sort of 'polluter pays' approach. In a poll published in September 1989 some 70 per cent of respondents agreed that the government should give a higher priority to environmental policy even if this means higher prices for some goods. Only 14 per cent disagreed.[5]

There is increasing support too for the principle that energy should be taxed so that its price should at least partially reflect the external costs of pollution, and in so doing, help pay for the means of reducing such pollution. Rather than trying to resist energy taxation, we should implement it in a way that avoids penalising the poor. We must also stress that taxation is not the only, or indeed the most important means of increasing energy efficiency. Regulatory means are likely to prove more effective in a wide number of areas.

So far I have discussed the nature and relative importance of different regulatory instruments, fiscal mechanisms and structural reforms. But however much such proposals are refined they are of little use unless we also have political vehicles to ensure their implementation.

POLITICAL PARTIES

I have already criticised the Conservative government for its unwillingness to implement firm interventionist measures to encourage energy efficiency and its reluctance to do more than pay lip service to the development of renewable energy sources.

Despite Mrs Thatcher's rhetorical conversion to the cause of saving the planet, many Conservatives remain unwilling to provide real support for efforts to combat global ecological threats, seeing such causes as being the preserve of the left.

On the other hand there are many 'turquoise Tories' whose opinions are gaining ground. We should remember that the Select Committee on Energy, whose enquiry into the energy policy implications of the greenhouse effect attacked the government's unwillingness to take interventionist action, has a Conservative majority. Tory 'wets' are increasingly using environmental issues as a stick to beat the free market anti-interventionist ideology that has dominated the Conservative Party since Mrs Thatcher's succession to the leadership. In a Bow Group pamphlet Tony Paterson, a member of the council of the World Wide Fund for Nature and a former Tory parliamentary candidate, has advocated a wide range of interventionist measures designed to achieve green objectives.[6] He observes that the 'Green Bill' is unlikely to satisfy voter expectations and calls for much stronger action.

However, the personalities and economic interests that dominate the Departments of Energy and Transport as I write mean that progress is likely to be slow. It is conceivable that increasing public demands for energy conservation may produce concessions in policy areas such as energy labelling, but it is more likely that if near term policy changes come, it will be because of legislative proposals at a European level which the Conservative government would have to accept, just as it was forced to accede to European initiatives to limit pollution from power stations and cars.

The greenhouse effect has often been cited by Tory leaders as a reason for supporting nuclear power. However, Conservative support for nuclear power is more firmly rooted in their desire for energy security against what they see as external and internal threats. Anything that appears to support nuclear energy and damn the miners acts to confirm already deeply-held political prejudices, although the government did have some second thoughts about completely destroying the British coal industry

Figure 6.2

with imported coal because of government plans to privatise the coal industry after the next election.

The anti-nuclear movement has been very weak among the Tories, but the sheer cost of dealing with the environmental consequences of nuclear power is concentrating many minds.

The Conservative attachment to nuclear power has been a barrier to efforts to push them into action on global warming; it has lulled them into a state where they see nuclear expansion as an effective answer to global warming (which it is not), and distracts their attention from the alternatives which require sometimes ideologically unpalatable intervention in the market.

By contrast, the Labour Party is ideologically committed to intervening in the market to secure social objectives, although environmental objectives have not yet been pushed as far up Labour's political agenda as greens would like. Labour's philosophy of caring for others could be broadened to include caring for the planet. Labour's interest in new forms of social ownership could make it more receptive to decentralised, localised forms of collectivism such as I have advocated.

Labour made the lack of provision for energy conservation a focal point of its attack on the government's electricity privatisation, but the party needs to give a much higher priority to specific proposals on energy efficiency and also to schemes to promote renewable energy sources. On the other hand it must try to balance its political sympathy with the coal miners with the need for energy policies that are sustainable in a world threatened with global warming.

Although the Labour Party's 1989 Policy Review statement denounced the government's support for increasing reliance on nuclear power as a means of tackling global warming as 'a transparent piece of opportunism',[7] and described a policy of gradually diminishing dependence on nuclear power, anti-nuclear activists are disappointed by the lack of a firm commitment to cancel all new nuclear power stations that have been ordered by the time a Labour government takes office.

The Transport and General Workers Union has come out against phasing out nuclear power, and the pro-nuclear lobby in the Labour Party remains strong. The chief worry of the unions is jobs. Yet those who worry about jobs at Sellafield should look to West Germany where at Wackersdorf a reprocessing plant has been turned into a project producing socially useful products. This is much more positive than churning out plutonium and nuclear waste.

Labour is still held back by conservative industrially-based interest groups who slow down progress towards sustainable energy and transport policies, but there are signs that progress is being made. There are increasingly powerful voices inside the party for the abandonment of road building programmes, for restrictions on car use in urban areas and for a greater emphasis on reforming motor vehicle taxation to promote fuel efficiency.

The Democrats have, since their former existence as Liberals, long supported large elements of an alternative energy strategy, lending support to energy conservation and renewables. They have given a high profile to green issues, even though on close examination their policies are less radical than they at first appear. They favour the phasing out of nuclear power, although the leadership's interpretation of what this means is rather more elastic than that of many Democrat activists.

The Democrats' erstwhile allies, the SDP, have been less enthusiastic about phasing out nuclear power than the Liberals in the old Alliance. They insisted that the Alliance 1987 manifesto contained a commitment to keep up research into fast breeder reactors.

The Green Party's commitments on energy policy have been more specific than other parties, with pledges to close all nuclear reactors within four years, create district energy authorities to implement local conservation schemes, set standards for electrical appliances, and introduce renewable energy supplies. They are certainly the only party to have favoured an energy tax at the 1987 election.

Although the Green Party proclaims that economic growth and sustainability are incompatible, many of the policies that it advocates could be, and to some small degree already are being, adopted by the 'growthist' establishment parties. But regardless of whether growth is or is not compatible with sustainability, many people see that there can often be a conflict between unrestrained materialism and ecological sustainability. This group of people is becoming larger and they are less worried about the Green Party's anti-growthist position than the failure of other parties to make sustainability an absolute rather than conditional priority over materialism.

The implementation of practical green policies in the context of an egalitarian, democratic approach is what is most important, regardless of the party label attached to the policies. In winning over people to sustainable policies and practices greens should promote lifestyles that rely less on materialism and more on caring for both people and the environment. This might be better achieved, and the planet more assuredly saved, by seeking to mobilise a majority committed to 'sustainable growth' rather than a minority pledged to oppose growth on principle.

Greens of all shades should not underestimate the degree to which industrial society could be reformed to incorporate decentralised ideas like smaller schools or community-oriented shopping and other services. Green socialists should promote practical schemes for decentralised forms of social ownership, including workers' co-operatives. This means counterposing Thatcherism's self-centred, over-materialistic enterprise culture with a caring and sharing co-operative enterprise culture.

CONCLUSION

Although practically every part of the political spectrum now rings with calls to care for the planet, and to meet the global ecological challenges among which the greenhouse effect is perhaps the most daunting, there is still a reluctance to translate this into firm action.

Many people are wary of adopting many of the radical policies I have suggested for fear that those who warn of global warming will be proved to have been crying wolf. The theoretical basis for predictions of global warming is in fact longstanding. If we wait until the already accumulating evidence becomes irrefutable, we may well have already committed the world to violent changes in climate and sea levels.

People cannot afford to claim that the gains of climatic change will outweigh the losses, for it is the change itself and the rate of change that is the most destabilising force.

Furthermore most, if not all, of the policies I have advocated are justifiable on grounds other than the need to combat global warming. The sooner we adopt a strategy relying on energy conservation and renewable energy the more easily we can avoid the perils of a nuclear future, resource depletion and various other types of environmental pollution.

Since there is so much that can be done that does not reduce our ability to continue improving living standards, we have very little excuse for delaying the adoption of a sustainable energy strategy. Nevertheless, combating the threat of global warming will require changes in lifestyles and the swallowing of unpalatable ideological medicine by all sections of the political spectrum.

The practical details of a sustainable strategy are becoming clearer, although we badly need to clarify our ideas on the relative importance of energy conservation and renewables, and on the role of energy taxation and how to implement these policies in an egalitarian way. We also need to pay a lot more attention to using the institutions of the European Community to advance the cause of ecological sustainability.

The green movement contains a rich bed of new ideas that can not only inspire people but can also be put into practice. We should resist the desire to become involved in solely abstract debates and concentrate on changing policies and lifestyles in a practical way. We must do this *now*. We have no time to lose.

Glossary

PJ petajoule (a thousand million million or 10^{15} joules)
KW kilowatt (a thousand watts or a thousand joules per second)
MW megawatt (million watts)
GW gigawatt (thousand million watts)
TW terawatt (million million watts)
TWH terawatt hour (quantity of energy produced in one hour by a terawatt of power)
GWe a gigawatt of electricity. A modern coal power station would produce about 1 GWe.
MTCE million tonne of coal equivalent (the amount of heat produced by burning one million tonnes of coal)
W/m²/°C watts per square metre per degree centigrade. This measures the rate of which heat is lost through say, a wall. The higher the figure the greater the thermal inefficiency.
Primary energy refers to total fuel use; because of conversion, transmission and other losses, it is greater than the energy 'delivered' to the consumer.

Notes

Chapter 1: Energy and sustainability

1. Throughout this book I use the terms 'greenhouse effect' and 'global warming' interchangeably to mean the same thing, although strictly speaking the greenhouse effect exists quite independently of human activity. The levels of carbon dioxide in the atmosphere regulate the planet's atmospheric temperature, and without any carbon dioxide global mean temperatures would be some 33°C lower. Further information on the nature and implications of the greenhouse effect can be gleaned from, in particular:

Bolin B., B. R., Doos, J. Jager and R. A. Warrick (eds.), *The Greenhouse Effect, Climatic Change and Ecosystems*. Chichester, J. Wiley and Son, 1986.

Boyle, S., and J. Ardill, *The Greenhouse Effect*, London, New English Library, 1989.

Pearce, F., *Turning up the Heat*, London, The Bodley Head, 1989.

2. Porritt, J., and D. Winner, *The Coming of the Greens*, London, Fontana, 1988, pp. 9–13.

3. World Commission on Environment and Development, *Our Common Future.*, Oxford, Oxford University Press, 1987, p. 8.

4. Porter, A., M. Spence, and R. Thompson, *The Energy Fix*, London, Pluto Press, 1986, p. 83.

5. House of Commons Select Committee on Energy, *Energy Policy Implications of the Greenhouse Effect*, London, HMSO, 1989.

6. Hall, T., *Nuclear Politics*, Harmondsworth, Penguin, 1986, p. 173.

7. Mintzer, I., *A Matter of Degrees*, Washington, DC., World Resources Institute, 1987.

8. Gribbin, J., 'End of the Ice Ages?', *New Scientist*, 17 June 1989 pp. 48–52.

9. F. Krause and others in a paper for the Dutch government cited by Energy and Environment Research Unit, Open University, *The Greenhouse Effect and Energy Policy*. Evidence to the House of Commons Enquiry into the Energy Policy Implications of the Greenhouse Effect, p. 49.

Chapter 2: Nuclear Power is no answer

1. Keepin, B., and G. Kats, *Greenhouse Warming. A rationale for Nuclear Power?*. Snowmass, Colorado, USA, Rocky Mountain Institute, 1989.

2. Collier, J., and L. Davies, *Chernobyl*. Barnwood, Gloucester, Central Electricity Generating Board, 1986, p. 18.

3. Cope, D., and P. James, *Earthing Electricity*, London, United Kingdom Centre for Economic and Environmental Development, 1988, pp. 28–29.

4. Mortimer, N., Addendum to *Friends of the Earth. Memorandum to House of Commons Select Committee on Energy's Enquiry into the Energy Policy Implications of the Greenhouse Effect*, London, Friends of the Earth, 1989.

5. The term total resources refers to the quantity of a particular energy source that is thought to exist and which might reasonably be expected to be recoverable. The term speculative resources refers to quantities which may exist in lower grade ores which are not economically recoverable at present, but may be in the future. To put this into context, the energy available from uranium resources used in conventional reactors is very much smaller than that available from oil resources.

6. Holmes, A., 'High prices put paid to a 20-year nuclear dream', *Financial Times*, November 11, 1989, p. 6.

7. Atkinson, A., 'The Environmental Impact of Nuclear Fusion', *Energy Policy*, Vol. 17 no. 3, pp. 277–283.

8. M. Spicer MP, Junior Energy Minister, in answer to Parliamentary Question number 1181 tabled by Elliot Morley MP, 10 July 1989.

9. Jackson, T., 'Is fusion feasible? An assessment of the methodology and policy implications', *Energy Policy*, Vol. 17 No. 4., p. 413.

Chapter 3: Conserving Energy

1. M. Spicer, MP, cited by A. Warren, in 'The Fifth Fuel', *Energy Today*, May 1989.

2. Friends of the Earth Memorandum on Greenhouse Effect, op. cit., p. 9.

3. Lucas, N., *Western European Energy Policies*, Oxford, Oxford University Press, 1985, p. 226.

4. Roberts, S., *Setting Standards for Efficiency*, London, Friends of the Earth, 1989.

5. 'The Good Bulb Guide', *Which?*, July 1987, p. 324.

6. *Friends of the Earth Memorandum to House of Lords European Communities Committee Enquiry into the Efficiency of Electricity Use*. London, Friends of the Earth, 1989.

7. *TVA Energy Services Report*. Chatanooga, Tennessee Valley Authority, 1987.

8. Energy and Environment Research Unit, *op. cit.*, p. 26.

9. Environmental Resources Ltd., for the Association for the Conservation of Energy (ACE), *Jobs and Energy Conservation*, London, ACE, 1983, p. 10.

10. Matthews G., S. Hodgkinson, and M. Fergusson, *Heat Planning for Need*, Stevenage, South East Economic Development Strategy, 1988, p. 28.

11. Olivier, D., H. Miall, et. al., *Energy Efficient Futures*, London, Earth Resources Research, 1983.

12. Department of Transport, *Roads for Prosperity*. Cmnd 693, London, HMSO, 1989.

13. Bleviss, D., *The New Oil Crisis and Fuel Economy Technologies*, New York, Quorum Books, 1988.

14. 'One for the Road?', *Economist*, 1 July 1989, p. 84.

15. House of Commons Select Committee on Energy, *op. cit.*, p. 54.

16. Leach, G., et al, *A Low Energy Strategy for the UK*, London, International Institute for Environment and Development, 1979.

Chapter 4: Supplying Energy

1. Sullivan, K. M., *The Effect of Carbon Dioxide Emissions from Coal Fired Power Plants, A Review in Perspective*. London, International Coal Development Institute, 1988, p. 7.

2. Grubb, M. J., *On Coefficients for Determining Greenhouse Gas Emmissions from Fossil Fuel Production*. Paper presented to the Paris IEA/OECD Energy Seminar on Greenhouse Emissions, Paris, April, 1989, London, Royal Institute for International Affairs, 1989.

3. Holger-Rogner, H., 'Technology and the prospects for natural gas', *Energy Policy*, Vol. 16 No. 1, pp. 9–25. See also Odell, P., 'The West European Gas Market', *Energy Policy*, Vol. 16 No. 5, pp. 480–493 for some similar comments.

4. Hohmeyer, O., *Social Costs of Energy Consumption*, Berlin, Springer/Verlag, 1988, p. 3.

5. Department of Energy, *Renewable Energy in the UK, The Way Forward*, Energy Paper 55. London, HMSO, 1988, p. 2.

6. British Nuclear Fuels advertisement in *New Statesman and Society*, 7 September 1989.

7. Clarke, A., *Windfarm Location and Environmental Impact*. Milton Keynes, Network for Alternative Technology and Technology Assessment, 1988, p. 128.

8. Grubb, M. J., *A Resource and Siting Analysis for Wind Energy in Britain*, London, Royal Institute for International Affairs, 1989.

9. House of Lords Select Committee on the European Communities, *Alternative Energy Sources, Report with Evidence*, London, HMSO, 1988, p. 19.

10. Flood, M., *Energy Without End*, London, Friends of the Earth, 1986, p. 25.

11. Grubb, M. J., *The Integrated Analysis of New Energy Sources on the British Supply System: Methods and Application*. Paper presented to the IEE Energy Options Conference, Reading, April 1987. London, Imperial College of Science and Technology, 1987, p. 3.
12. Interview with Bernard Wilkins, 24 July 1989.
13. Interview with Steve Newman, 30 October 1989.
14. Department of Energy, *op. cit.*, p. 4.
15. Flood, M., *Solar prospects*. London, Wildwood House, 1983, p. 133.
16. Joyce, C., 'Keeping the World Cool with Deep Heat', *New Scientist*, 4 February 1989, pp. 58–63.

Chapter 5: Energy Futures

1. I have used the total of energy demanded in Olivier's A2 scenario as the basis for the 'Moderate' scenario, although I have used a different pattern of energy supply.
2. This table is loosely based on the likely contribution of renewables mentioned in Flood's, *Energy Without End*, op. cit., p. 25. Michael Flood gave lower estimates for the potential of tidal power and biomass.
3. Jackson, T., and A. Atkinson, *The Technical and Economic Comparison of Non-Fossil Fuelled Electricity Supply Options*. Evidence to Hinkley 'C' Nuclear Power Station Inquiry. Hinkley, Somerset, Consortium of Opposing Local Authorities, 1988.
4. I have used the total of energy demanded in Oliver's A1 scenario as the basis for the 'Radical' scenario, although I have used a different pattern of energy supply.
5. Boyle, S., L. Taylor and I. Brown, *Solving the Greenhouse Dilemma* Association for the Conservation of Energy and the World Wide Fund for Nature, 1989, p. 17.

Chapter 6: Political Means

1. Holmes, A., J. Chesshire, and S. Thomas, *Power on the Market*. Falmer, Brighton, Science Policy Research Unit, University of Sussex, 1987, pp. 123–125.
2. Atkinson, A., *After Chernobyl*, Stevenage, South East Economic Development Strategy, 1987, pp. 172–182.
3. Von Weizsacker, E., *Global Warming and Environmental Taxes*. Paper to the Turin Conference on 'Atmosphere, Climate and Man'. London, Institute for European Environmental Policy, 1989, p. 10.
4. Road Transport Research, *Challenges and Opportunities for Transport*. Paris, Organisation for Economic Co-operation and Development, 1989, p. 47.
5. ICM Opinion Poll, *The Guardian*, 18 September 1989, p. 20.
6. Paterson, T., *The Green Conservative*, London, Bow Group, 1989.
7. *Meet the Challenge, Make the Change*, Final Report of Labour's Policy Review for the 1990s, London, Labour Party, 1989.

Index